3rd edition

THE CHEMICAL MAZE

Shopping Companion

About the Author

Bill Statham lives with his wife and business partner Kay Lancashire on the Far South Coast of New South Wales. He is a researcher, writer and publisher with an interest in health education and committed to making a positive difference to the health of people and the environment.

Bill studied and practised homeopathy both in Australia and England for over ten years. During this time he became increasingly concerned about the detrimental effects on people's health caused by synthetic chemicals in the foods we eat and products we use every day.

Bill wrote The Chemical Maze to make it simpler and easier for people to recognise those additives and ingredients in foods, personal care products and cosmetics having the potential to cause discomfort and ill-health. With this recognition comes freedom of choice, and for many a new lease on life.

3rd edition

THE CHEMICAL MAZE

Shopping Companion

YOUR GUIDE
TO
FOOD ADDITIVES
AND
COSMETIC INGREDIENTS

Bill Statham

POSSIBILITY.COM

First published in 2001 -1 reprint
2nd edition published in 2002 - 5 reprints
This edition published September 2005 / Second printing December 2005
by POSSIBILITY.COM

National Library of Australia Cataloguing-in-Publication Data:

Statham, Bill, 1955-
The chemical maze shopping companion: your guide to food additives and cosmetic ingredients.
3rd ed.
Bibliography.
ISBN 0 9578535 3 X.

1. Food additives - Handbooks, manuals, etc. 2. Cosmetics - Handbooks, manuals, etc. 3. Chemicals - Handbooks, manuals, etc. I. Title.

540

Cover design by Kay Lancashire

Printed in Australia by The Northern Star

Disclaimer

Every effort has been made to ensure that the information in this book is accura and current at the time of publication. Several resources were consulted and cros referenced. The book does not claim to include all information about all chemica used in foods, cosmetics and personal care products. The author and the publish disclaim liability for any misuse or misunderstanding of any information containe herein and disclaims liability for all loss, damage or injury, be it health, financial otherwise, suffered by any individual or group acting upon or relying on informatic contained herein. A qualified health practitioner should be consulted in all cases of health.

Dedication

To my father Arthur, and my late mother Dorne,
for always believing in me.

"The mind, once enlightened, cannot again become dark"

-Thomas Paine, *Common Sense*-

Table of Contents

Preface

This is now the third edition of The Chemical Maze and the demand for the information it contains continues to grow. With sales of over 37,000 copies, it seems that there is an increasing awareness of the potential harm that certain chemicals in foods and cosmetic products can inflict on people's health and the environment. Safer and more natural substances can, in most instances, replace these human and environmental 'pollutants'.

Apart from being completely revised and updated, there have been a number of changes to this edition of your guide. Firstly, there has been a slight name change. 'Shopping Companion' is, we feel, an appropriate addition to the title. Other changes include the addition of over twenty pages of ingredients to section 2, and information about the environmental impact of many of the chemicals has also been included. Identification of ANIMAL derived and GM additives and ingredients is included together with a glossary of terms, acronyms and definitions.

A Bookshelf Companion will soon be available with all the information contained in the Shopping Companion and much more.

We hope that The Chemical Maze Shopping Companion - Your Guide to Food Additives and Cosmetic Ingredients helps you on the road to good health and we thank you for your ongoing support.

Bill and Kay, August 2005

How to Use Your Guide

The reference part of this book is divided into two sections. Section one provides a numerical list of food additives approved for use in Australia and New Zealand. If you know only the name of a food additive, then refer to the alphabetical list of food additives to find its code number.

Section two lists in alphabetical order ingredients that may be found in cosmetics and personal care products.

Each section gives useful and relevant information about the additives and ingredients listed.

Column one in section one gives the code number of each food additive. Column one in section two gives the names of many ingredients found in cosmetic and personal care products. In most cases the origin of each additive/ ingredient is also given including whether it may be of ANIMAL origin or a product of genetic modification (GM).

Column two in section one gives the name of the additive.

Column three in section one (column two in section two) gives one or more functions of the additive/ingredient.

Column four in section one (column three in section two) indicates by a face code just how user-friendly each additive/ingredient is from *safe and/or beneficial* through to *hazardous.* **Note: The evaluation given is the opinion of the author at the time of writing based on available researched information.**

This information was referenced from several sources, including Material Safety Data Sheets, university studies and, medical and scientific laboratory reports. The codes shown are only a general guide, as individuals react differently to chemical exposures. The type and severity of reaction will depend on many factors. A few of these are: the health of the person, the amounts to which they are exposed and the period of exposure, the environment in which the person lives/works and the persons age and sex. However, it is recommended that only those products containing additives and ingredients that are *safe and/or beneficial* or *safe for most people* as indicated by the happy faces be chosen.

☺☺	2 happy faces = *safe and/or beneficial*
☺	1 happy face = *safe for most people*
😐**?**	1 quizzical face = *caution advised*
☹	1 sad face = *best avoided*
☹☹	2 sad faces = *hazardous*

Column five in section one (column four in section two) lists some of the benefits of the additive/ingredient and/or some of the detrimental effects, symptoms and illnesses it has the **potential** to either cause or exacerbate. Note: where certain specific medical disorders including cancer, diabetes, tumours and others are mentioned, only limited reference is made as to whether occurrence was in animals or humans. Also, usually no reference is made to the amounts or concentration of chemicals involved, types of exposure or time periods involved. This information is far beyond the scope of this book and the reader is referred to the bibliography if they wish to find out more information.

Column six in section one (column five in section two) lists a few relevant common consumer products that may contain that particular additive/ingredient.

Column seven in section one (column six in section two) lists some other uses for that particular additive/ingredient.

Introduction

The idea for this book was born out of a need to understand how some chemicals that are a part of our everyday lives may play a part in ill health. Whilst in practice as a homoeopathic practitioner I often wondered why some of my patients would regain their health under treatment only to relapse some time later. It was only after some research that I made the connection between what my patients were eating, not just the types of foods, but also, and often more significantly, the chemical food additives that they contained, and their health problems. I also investigated whether there was a possibility that the products they used on their bodies every day, personal care and cosmetic products, could also have a detrimental effect on their health. What I discovered during my research amazed and often alarmed me. I discovered that a significant number of chemicals added to foods and cosmetics could cause or exacerbate health problems such as asthma, dermatitis, hives, migraines, hay fever, gastric upsets, behavioural problems, hyperactivity, learning difficulties and many others. Some of these chemicals are found to be toxic to body organs and systems like the liver, kidneys, heart, thymus and brain, and the immune, nervous, hormonal, reproductive and endocrine systems. Even more disturbing was the fact that some chemicals, which are permitted in foods, personal care products and cosmetics could also cause birth defects, genetic mutations, cancer and damage to DNA.

I began to tell my patients of my discoveries and encouraged them to eliminate, as much as possible, the chemicals that were found to have detrimental effects on health. I was not disappointed by the results of this exercise. Indeed, as I had expected, the health of my patients improved dramatically and often surprised even the patients themselves. An interesting side effect happened as well. Those patients who enrolled their families and friends into this new lifestyle, by eliminating harmful chemicals, were reporting that the health and well-being of these people was also improving, sometimes dramatically so.

I came to the decision that perhaps I should write a booklet so that many more people could benefit from this knowledge. I had envisioned a credit card sized guide that would fit in the wallet! It wasn't long into the research that I realized that the information would "overflow" such a small format. I ploughed on with my research and after another twelve months I felt I had enough information to publish a small shopping guide.

The first edition of this book, which I called The Chemical Maze – Your Guide to Food Additives and Cosmetic Ingredients, was self-published in Australia in April 2001. Four years later, in 2005, over 37,000 copies have been sold, mostly in Australia and New Zealand.

I receive many letters and emails from people telling me how their health and the health of their children has improved after using the book to eliminate harmful chemicals from their lives. I am often touched and inspired by the stories they tell, like the following from Debra in Sydney. *"I would like to share with you a miracle with my youngest son Jack. By eliminating harmful numbers from our environment, house and food my son's behaviour has become much calmer, he is so much easier to handle. The main difference that we welcomed was that Jack was diagnosed a classic ADHD with major learning difficulties (not that I ever put him in that box) and this is the first time that anything alternative had actually made a huge difference for him. His memory is getting better each day and he is all of a sudden able to learn. His Rudolf Steiner schoolteacher is amazed at the dramatic difference and suddenly."*

Many of the foods, personal care products and cosmetics marketed towards us today contain the chemical additives and ingredients you will find listed in this book. There will, of course, be many others that are not listed, as manufacturers can choose from many thousands of chemicals for use in their products. A frightening number of these chemicals have never been adequately tested for long-term effects on human health. In addition, there are food additives and ingredients in use that some countries have banned.

Looking on the positive side, there are an increasing number of companies producing foods and cosmetic products without harmful numbers and synthetic chemicals. So we do have choices and with a little bit of guidance and a determination to act we can avoid the nasties and lead healthier lives. The price of ignorance and apathy can be very high indeed. We do not have to pay that price.

Our existence on this planet may well depend on the decisions we make and the actions we take today. Many species have disappeared forever due to a radical change in their environment. Could the gross contamination, with persistent toxic chemicals, of our soils; our water, the air we breathe and indeed our bodies lead to the disappearance of the human species? **Now is the time to act!**

SECTION 1

FOOD ADDITIVES

Number	Names	Functions	Code	Potential Effects	Possible Food Use	Other Uses
100	**CURCUMIN OR TURMERIC** (derived from *curcuma longa*, an East Indian herb)	Colouring (orange /yellow) Antioxidant	☺	Curcumin has many beneficial health effects; may cause skin irritation; moderately toxic by injection	Processed foods	Supplements, marking ink, fabric dye
101	**RIBOFLAVIN; RIBOFLAVIN-5'-PHOSPHATE SODIUM** (may be of **ANIMAL** origin; may be **GM**)	Colouring (orange /yellow)	☺☺	Regarded as safe in food use; has many beneficial health effects	Processed foods	Cosmetics, vitamin tablets, used in emollients
102	**TARTRAZINE** FD & C Yellow No. 5 (coal tar dye; banned in some countries)	Colouring (lemon-yellow to orange)	☹☹	Asthma; urticaria; dermatitis; headache; hay fever; concentration difficulties; depression; skin rash; learning difficulties; behavioural problems; swelling of lips and tongue; hyperactivity; aggressive behaviour; insomnia; confusion; anaphylaxis; aspirin sensitive people may wish to avoid; NRC; carcinogenic	Beverages, processed foods	Cosmetics, wool and silk dye, drugs

Number	Names	Functions	Code	Potential Effects	Possible Food Use	Other Uses
103	**ALKANET OR ALKANNIN** (from a herb-like tree-root; banned in the USA)	Colouring (red - copper - blue)	😐?	The FDA withdrew approval for use in foods in the USA in 1988	Processed foods, sausage casings	Cosmetics, hair oil, inks
104	**QUINOLINE YELLOW** (synthetic; azo dye; may be of **ANIMAL** origin; banned in some countries)	Colouring (dull yellow to greenish yellow)	☹	Asthma; urticaria; skin rash; hyperactivity; anaphylaxis; aspirin sensitive people may wish to avoid; carcinogenic	Beverages, processed foods	Cosmetic dye, lipsticks, soap, toothpaste, hair products, medications
110	**SUNSET YELLOW FCF**, (FD & C Yellow No.6; synthetic; azo dye; bannedin some countries)	Colouring (yellow)	☹☹	Asthma; urticaria, hay fever; abdominal pain; eczema; hives; hyperactivity; aspirin sensitive people may wish to avoid; carcinogenic	Beverages, processed foods	Cosmetics, hair rinses, oral medications, Ventolin syrup
120	**COCHINEAL OR CARMINES OR CARMINIC ACID** (cochineal and carminic acid restricted in some countries; **ANIMAL** origin)	Colouring (red)	☹	Asthma; anaphylaxis (possibily life-threatening); urticaria; aspirin sensitive people may wish to avoid; hay fever	Processed foods	Cosmetics, red eye shadow, shampoo, mascaras
122	**AZORUBINE OR CARMOISINE** (azo dye; banned in some countries)	Colouring (red)	☹	Asthma; hyperactivity; aspirin sensitive people may wish to avoid; animal carcinogen	Beverages, processed foods	

Number	Names	Functions	Code	Potential Effects	Possible Food Use	Other Uses
123	**AMARANTH** (the synthetic chemical not the grain; FD & C Red No.2; coal tar dye and azo dye; banned in some countries)	Colouring (bluish red)	☹☹	Hyperactivity; urticaria; asthma; rhinitis; aspirin sensitive people may wish to avoid; may affect reproduction, liver, kidneys, birth defects, carcinogenic; teratogen	Ice cream, edible ices, chutney, jams, spreads, fruit juice, jelly, confectionery, flavoured drinks, wine based drinks	Lipstick, rouge, other cosmetics
124	**PONCEAU 4R** (cochineal red A; monoazo dye; banned in some countries)	Colouring (red)	☹	Asthma; hay fever; hyperactivity; aspirin sensitive people may wish to avoid; carcinogenic	Beverages, processed foods	Mouthwash, hair rinse
127	**ERYTHROSINE** (FD & C Red No.3; coal tar dye; banned in some countries)	Colouring (bluish pink)	☹☹	Asthma; hyperactivity; urticaria; learning difficulties; light sensitivity; may affect liver, heart, thyroid, reproduction, stomach; carcinogenic	Maraschino cherries, cocktail cherries, glace cherries	Toothpaste, dental disclosing tablets, rouge, medications
129	**ALLURA RED AC** (FD & C Red No.40; coal tar dye; banned in some countries)	Colouring (orange/red)	☹	Asthma; hyperactivity; allergic reactions; hay fever; urticaria; aspirin sensitive people may wish to avoid; adverse reproductive effects in animals; carcinogenic	Beverages, processed foods	Cosmetics, lipstick, medications

Number	Names	Functions	Code	Potential Effects	Possible Food Use	Other Uses
132	**INDIGOTINE** (Indigo carmine; FD & C Blue No.2; coal tar dye; banned in some countries)	Colouring (moderate bright green)	☹	Asthma; allergic reactions; hyperactivity; heart problems; NRC; carcinogenic; *see Coal Tar in section 2*	Beverages, processed foods	Hair rinses, dye in kidney function tests, tablets and capsules
133	**BRILLIANT BLUE FCF** (FD & C Blue No.1; coal tar dye; banned in some countries)	Colouring (bright blue)	☹☹	Asthma; urticaria; hay fever; NRC; allergic reactions; aspirin sensitive people may wish to avoid; carcinogenic	Beverages, processed foods	Toothpaste, cosmetics, hair dye, deodorant
140	**CHLOROPHYLL** (green colouring in plants; extracted using MEK, acetone, ethanol and dichloromethane)	Colouring (olive to dark green)	☺	Regarded as safe in food use; has beneficial health effects; can cause a sensitivity to light	Processed foods	Antiperspirant, deodorant, mouthwash, supplements, medicines
141	**CHLOROPHYLL COPPER COMPLEX; CHLOROPHYLL-IN COPPER COMPLEX** (may be synthetic)	Colouring (bright green)	☺☺	Regarded as safe in food use	Processed foods	
142	**GREEN S** (Coal tar dye; banned in some countries)	Colouring (green)	☹	Hyperactivity; asthma; skin rashes; insomnia; *see Coal Tar in section 2*	Beverages, processed foods	Textile industry

Number	Names	Functions	Code	Potential Effects	Possible Food Use	Other Uses
143	**FAST GREEN FCF** (synthetic; FD&C Green No.3)	Colouring (sea green)	☹	Sensitisation in allergenic people; caused malignant tumours in rats when injected under the skin; bladder tumours	Beverages, processed foods	Cosmetics, except those used near the eyes
150a	**CARAMEL I** (plain caramel; may be from sugar beet, sugar cane or corn starch; may be **GM**)	Colouring (dark brown)	😐?	Gastrointestinal problems; needs to be tested for mutagenic, teratogenic, subacute and reproductive effects	Wine, sparkling wine, fortified wine, beer, stout, fruit wines, mead, vegetable wines	Cosmetics, skin lotions
150b	**CARAMEL II** (caustic sulphite caramel; may be from sugar beet, sugar cane or corn starch; may be **GM**)	Colouring (dark brown to black)	😐?	Hyperactivity; may affect liver; stomach problems	Wine, sparkling wine, fortified wine, beer, stout, fruit wines, mead; vegetable wines	
150c	**CARAMEL III** (ammonia caramel; may be from sugar beet, sugar cane or corn starch; made using ammonia; may be **GM**)	Colouring (dark brown to black)	☹	Hyperactivity; may affect liver, stomach, reproduction; caused convulsions in some animal tests; blood toxicity in rats, lowered white cell counts in rats	Wine, sparkling wine, fortified wine, beer, stout, fruit wines, mead, vegetable wines	

Number	Names	Functions	Code	Potential Effects	Possible Food Use	Other Uses
150d	**CARAMEL** IV (sulphite ammonia caramel; may be from sugar beet, sugar cane or corn starch; ammonia and sulphite compounds; may be **GM**)	Colouring	☹	Hyperactivity; soft to liquid stools & increased bowel movements; blood toxicity in rats; inhibits metabolism of B6 in rabbits; serious doubts exist on safety	Stout, beer, wine, sparkling wine, fortified wine, fruit wines, vegetable wines, mead	Cosmetics, skin lotions, cigarettes
151	**BRILLIANT BLACK BN OR BRILLIANT BLACK PN** (azo dye; banned in many countries)	Colouring (black)	☹☹	Asthma; hyperactivity; may affect kidneys, stomach; NRC; carcinogenic	Beverages	Cosmetics
153	**CARBON BLACKS OR VEGETABLE CARBON** (usually from burnt vegetable matterr; may be of **ANIMAL** origin; may be **GM**; banned in some countries)	Colouring (black)	😐?	Mildly toxic by ingestion, skin contact and inhalation; may be carcinogenic	Processed foods	Cosmetics
155	**BROWN HT** (coal tar dye & azo dye; banned in some countries)	Colouring (brown)	☹	Asthma; allergic reactions; urticaria; NRC; may affect kidneys, aspirin sensitive people may wish to avoid	Processed foods, beverages	

Number	Names	Functions	Code	Potential Effects	Possible Food Use	Other Uses
160a	**CAROTENE** (mostly natural and of plant origin; may be of **ANIMAL** origin)	Colouring (orange to red)	☺☺	Regarded as safe in food use; may have beneficial health effects	Butter	Skin creams, supplements, animal feeds, cigarettes
160b	**ANNATTO EXTRACTS** (annatto is obtained from the annatto tree; bixin and norbixin are extracts)	Colouring (yellow to pink)	☹	May cause irritability and head banging in children; skin contact may cause urticaria and pruritis; hypotension; undergoing testing by industry due to a lack of toxicity data	Flavoured milk, ice cream, pasta, milk products, noodles, confectionery, cakes, pastries	Fabric dyes, soaps, varnish, body paints
160c	**PAPRIKA OLEORESINS** (extracted from peppers)	Colouring (orange to red)	☺☺	Regarded as safe in food use; may have beneficial health effects	Processed foods	Poultry feeds
160d	**LYCOPENE** (extracted from tomatoes and pink grapefruit; may be synthetic; may be **GE**)	Colouring (red)	☺☺	Regarded as safe in food use; may have beneficial health effects	Processed foods	Supplements
160e	**BETA-APO-8' CAROTENAL** (found naturally in fruits and vegetables; may be produced synthetically)	Colouring (orange to yellow/red)	☺☺	Regarded as safe in food use	Processed foods, butter	

Number	Names	Functions	Code	Potential Effects	Possible Food Use	Other Uses
160f	**BETA-APO-8' CAROTENOIC ACID OR METHYL ETHYL ESTER** (natural substance from plants)	Colouring (yellow to orange)	☺☺	Regarded as safe in food use	Processed foods	
161a	**FLAVOXANTHIN** (xanthophyll)	Colouring (yellow)	☺	Xanthophylls compete with carotenes for absorption into the body	Processed foods	
161b	**LUTEIN** (found in egg yoke, fat cells, green leaves; may be of **ANIMAL** origin)	Colouring (yellow to red)	☺☺	Regarded as safe in food use at low levels	Processed foods	Animal and poultry feeds
161c	**KRYPTOXANTHIN** (found in Cape Gooseberry, egg yoke, butter; may be of **ANIMAL** origin)	Colouring (yellow)	☺	Xanthophylls compete with carotenes for absorption into the body	Processed foods	
161d	**RUBIXANTHIN** (xanthophyll found in roeships)	Colouring (yellow)	☺	Xanthophylls compete with carotenes for absorption into the body	Processed foods	
161e	**VIOLOXANTHIN** (xanthophyll found in yellow pansies)	Colouring (yellow)	☺	Xanthophylls compete with carotenes for absorption into the body	Processed foods	

Number	Names	Function	Code	Potential Effects	Possible Food Use	Other Uses
161f	**RHODOXANTHIN** (xanthophyll found in the seeds of the yew tree)	Colouring (yellow)	☺	Xanthophylls compete with carotenes for absorption into the body	Processed foods	
162	**BEET RED** (extracted from beetroot)	Colouring (deep red/purple)	☺	Regarded as safe in food use; contains nitrates so NRC	Desserts, jellies, jams, liquorice, sweets	Cosmetics
163	**ANTHOCYANINS OR GRAPESKIN EXTRACT OR BLACKCURRANT EXTRACT**	Colouring (red/violet)	☺☺	Regarded as safe in food use; have many beneficial health effects	Wine, sparkling wine, fortified wine	Vitamin tablets, supplements, cosmetics
164	**SAFFRON OR CROCETIN OR CROCIN** (from the crocus plant)	Colouring (orange-brown)	☺	Regarded as safe in foods; beneficial health effects; anaphylaxis	Jellies, icing sugar, caviar, jams, tomato sauce, pickles	Cosmetics, perfumery, marking ink
170	**CALCIUM CARBONATE** (chalk, limestone, bones, marble, dolomite, coral; may be of **ANIMAL** origin)	Colouring (white) Abrasive	😐?	Regarded as safe in foods at low levels; can cause abdominal pain, nausea, constipation	Foods for infants, wine, sparkling wine, fortified wine, fruit wines, mead	Cosmetics, face powder, bleach, vitamin tablets, cigarettes
171	**TITANIUM DIOXIDE** (occurs naturally; may contain nanoparticles; *see Nanoparticles in section 2*)	Colouring (white) Opacifier	😐?	Regarded as safe in food use; skin contact may cause irritation; reproductive toxicity; limited evidence of cancer in animal studies	Pan sugar coated confectionery, sweets, chewing gum, icing sugar, jam, jellies	Bath powder, face powder, ointment, sun-screen, marker ink, paints

Number	Names	Functions	Code	Potential Effects	Possible Food Use	Other Uses
172	**IRON OXIDE** (rust; synthetic oxides of iron; banned in some countries)	Colouring (red/brown/ black/orange /yellow)	😐 ?	Iron is potentially toxic in all forms; excess intake can lead to an increased risk of numerous health conditions	Processed foods	Pet foods, dying egg shells, face powders, eye shadows
173	**ALUMINIUM** (extracted from the mineral ore bauxite)	Colouring (metallic)	☹	Ingestion or inhalation can aggrevate kidney & lung disorders; cardiovascular, reproductive, neurotoxicity; evidence of link with Alzheimer's; European Parliament said aluminium additives should be banned	External decoration on confectionery, liqueurs	Cosmetics, cooking pots and pans, antiperspirant, silver finish to pills and tablets
174	**SILVER** (naturally occuring metal)	Colouring (metallic)	😐 ?	Toxic in large doses; accumulates in tissues; kidney damage; argyria	External decoration on confectionery, liqueurs	Cosmetics, nail polish
175	**GOLD** (naturally occuring metal)	Colouring (metallic)	☺	Regarded as safe in food use; rare allergic reactions; neurotoxicity	External decoration on confectionery, liqueurs	Cosmetics
181	**TANNIC ACID; TANNINS** (tannins from oak, sumac and others)	Colouring (brown) Emulsifier	😐 ?	Thought to be a weak carcinogen; in creams - irritation and blistering	Wine, sparkling wine, fortified wine, fruit wines	Sunscreen, antiperspirant, eye lotion

Number	Names	Functions	Code	Potential Effects	Possible Food Use	Other Uses
200	**Sorbic acid** (may be from the berries of Mountain Ash or synthetic from chemicals)	Preservative Humectant	😐?	Allergic reactions; skin irritation; behavioural problems; erythema; asthma; contact dermatitis	Candied fruits, low joule jams, sugar confectionery, icings, noodles, pasta, breads	Cosmetics, mouthwash, toothpaste, ointments, dental cream
201	**Sodium sorbate** (sodium salt of sorbic acid)	Preservative	😐?	Allergic reactions; kidney, liver and blood pressure problems; fluid retention	Candied fruits, low joule jams, sugar confectionery, icings, noodles	Cosmetics, ointments
202	**Potassium sorbate** (potassium salt of sorbic acid)	Preservative	😐?	Allergic reactions; asthma; skin irritation; behavioural problems	Candied fruits, low joule jams, sugar confectionery	Cosmetics, ointments, cigarettes
203	**Calcium sorbate** (synthetic; derived from sorbic acid)	Preservative	😐?	Contact urticaria; skin irritation; asthma; allergic reactions; behavioural problems	Liquid ice confections, cheese and cheese products, low joule jams	Cosmetics, ointments
210	**Benzoic acid** (occurs in nature in cherry bark, raspberries, anise and cassia bark; may be made commercially from benzene)	Preservative	☹	Asthma; urticaria; hives behavioural problems; hyperactivity; may affect lungs; eye and skin irritation; aspirin sensitive people may wish to avoid; neurotoxicity	Low joule jams & spreads, cocktail cherries, glace cherries, chilli paste, maraschino cherries, icings, coconut milk	Cosmetics, hair rinse, skin cleansers, perfumes, Ventolin syrup, pharmaceuticals

Number	Names	Functions	Code	Potential Effects	Possible Food Use	Other Uses
211	**SODIUM BENZOATE** (sodium salt of benzoic acid)	Preservative	☹	Asthma; urticaria; contact dermatitis; hay fever; mouth and skin irritation; hyperactivity; anaphylaxis; aspirin sensitive people may wish to avoid	Low joule jams and spreads, cocktail cherries, glace cherries, chilli paste, maraschino cherries, icings, coconut milk	Toothpaste, eye creams, cosmetics, medical diagnostic aid for liver function
212	**POTASSIUM BENZOATE** (synthetic; potassium salt of benzoic acid)	Preservative	☹	Asthma; urticaria; eczema; allergic reactions; gastric irritation; aspirin sensitive people may wish to avoid	Low joule jams and spreads, cocktail cherries, glace cherries, chilli paste	Cosmetics
213	**CALCIUM BENZOATE** (calcium salt of benzoic acid)	Preservative	☹	Asthma; anaphylaxis; hyperactivity; nettle rash; behavioural problems; eczema; NRC; aspirin sensitive people may wish to avoid	Low joule jams and spreads, cocktail cherries, glace cherries, chilli paste, maraschino cherries, icings	Cosmetics
216	**PROPYLPARABEN OR PROPYL- p HYDROXYBENZOATE** (synthetic; ester of benzoic acid)	Preservative	☹	Asthma; urticaria; allergic reactions; skin redness, itching and swelling; anaphylaxis; *see Parabens section 2*	Preparations of food additives	Shampoos, eye lotions, bubble bath, foundation creams, baby preparations

Number	Names	Functions	Code	Potential Effects	Possible Food Use	Other Uses
218	**METHYLPARABEN OR METHYL- p HYDROXYBENZOATE** (synthetic; ester of benzoic acid)	Preservative	☹	Asthma; urticaria; allergic reactions; skin redness, itching and swelling; anaphylaxis; *see Parabens section 2*	Preparations of food additives	Cosmetics, skin and hair care products, baby preparations, suncreams
220	**SULPHUR DIOXIDE** (produced by burning sulphur)	Preservative	☹	Asthma; anaphylaxis; bronchospasm; hypo-tension; bronchitis; bronchoconstriction; destroys vitamins A and B1 in food; animal mutagen	Low joule jams and spreads, dried fruits & vegetables, desiccated coco-nut, immitation fruit, biscuits, cakes, pastries, pasta	Glue, disinfectant in breweries and food factories
221	**SODIUM SULPHITE** (synthetic; sodium salts of sulphurous acid; *see Sulphites in section* 2)	Preservative	☹	Skin rash; diarrhoea; gastric irritation; asthma; nausea; destroys vita-min B content in foods; those with poor liver or kidney function should avoid; may be hazard-ous to aquatic organisms	Flour products, cakes, cheese and cheese products, dried fruits, low joule jams and spreads, candied fruit, pastries	Hair dyes, used to bleach straw, silk and wool, developer in photography
222	**SODIUM BISULPHITE** (synthetic; *see Sulphites in section* 2)	Preservative	☹	Bronchial asthma; chronic urticaria; skin irritation; mutagenic	Processed fruits & vegetables, liquid ice confections	Mouthwashes, hair dyes, wart remover

Number	Names	Functions	Code	Potential Effects	Possible Food Use	Other uses
223	**SODIUM METABISULPHITE** (synthetic; *see Sulphites in section 2*)	Preservative	☹	Asthma (life threatening attacks); atopic dermatitis; hay fever; chronic urticaria; harmful to aquatic organisms	Cheese & cheese products, dried fruits, low joule jams and spreads	Cosmetics, hair products, underarm deodorants
224	**POTASSIUM METABISULPHITE** (*see Sulphites section 2*)	Preservative	☹	Asthma; gastric irritation; nettle rash; behavioural problems; anaphylaxis	Cheese & cheese products, dried fruits & vegetables	Cosmetics, bleaching straw, developing dye
225	**POTASSIUM SULPHITE** (*see Sulphites section 2*)	Preservative	☹	*See sodium sulphite (221)*	Cheese products, dried fruits	Cosmetics
228	**POTASSIUM BISULPHITE** (*see Sulphites section 2*)	Preservative	☹	Asthma; skin reactions; anaphylaxis; gastric irritation; hyperactivity	Frozen avocado, low joule jams, dried fruits	
234	**NISIN** (from the bacterium streptococcuc lactis)	Preservative	☹	The European Parliament said in 2003 that it should not be used as it could cause antibiotic resistance in humans	Dairy and fat based desserts, dips and snacks, coconut cream, coconut milk, sauces	
235	**NATAMYCIN; PIMARICIN** (from the bacterium streptomyces natalensis)	Preservative	☹	Moderately toxic by ingestion; vomiting; diarrhoea; anorexia; mild skin irritation	Uncooked fermented manufactured meats, cheese, cheese products	Drug used to treat fungal infections of the eyes & eyelids

Number	Names	Functions	Code	Potential Effects	Possible Food Use	Other Uses
242	**DIMETHYL DICARBONATE** (DMDC)	Preservative	☺ ☺	Regarded as safe in food use	Sport drinks, fruit drinks, instant teas, fruit wines	Yeast inhibiter in wine
249	**POTASSIUM NITRITE** (banned in some countries; *see Nitrites in section 2*)	Preservative Colour fixative	☹ ☹	Asthma; kidney inflammation; behavioural problems; headache; forms nitrosamines; not permitted in foods for babies under 6 months; inhibits oxygen in the blood; carcinogenic; teratogenic	Canned, cured, manufactured and pressed meats, sausages, bacon, poultry and game products	
250	**SODIUM NITRITE** (synthetic; banned in some countries; *see Nitrites in section 2*)	Preservative Colour fixative	☹ ☹	Nausea; vomiting; dizziness; headaches; not permitted in foods for babies less than 6 months; toxic to aquatic organisms; teratogenic	Canned, cured, manufactured and pressed meats, sausages, bacon, poultry and game products	Anticorrosive in some cosmetics
251	**SODIUM NITRATE** (sodium salt of nitric acid; banned in some countries; *see Nitrites in section 2*)	Preservative Colour fixative	☹ ☹	Nausea; vomiting; dizziness; headaches; migraine; may affect thyroid gland; not permitted in foods for babies less than 6 months	Cheese & cheese products, slow dried cured meats, fermented, uncooked, processed and diced meats	Matches, fertiliser, tobacco

Number	Names	Functions	Code	Potential Effects	Possible Food Use	Other Uses
252	**POTASSIUM NITRATE** (banned in some countries; *see Nitrites in section 2*)	Preservative Colour fixative	☹☹	Asthma; kidney inflammation; behavioural problems; dizziness; headache; forms nitrosamines *(see section 2)*; not permitted in foods for babies under 6 months; teratogenic	Cheese & cheese products, slow dried cured meats, fermented, uncooked, processed and diced meats	Matches, gunpowder, tobacco
260	**ACETIC ACID, GLACIAL** (occurs naturally in a variety of fruits and plants)	Acidity regulator	☺	Regarded as safe in food use; skin irritation; hives; skin rash; caused cancer in rats and mice orally and by injection; harmful to aquatic organisms	Fruit wine, mead, vegetable wine, foods for infants	Animal feeds, hair dyes, hand lotions, cigarettes
261	**POTASSIUM ACETATE OR POTASSIUM DIACETATE** (potassium salt of acetic acid)	Acidity regulator	😐?	People with impaired kidney function or cardiac disease may wish to avoid	Foods for infants, processed foods	Diuretic and heart medications
262	**SODIUM ACETATE OR SODIUM DIACETATE** (compound of sodium acetate and acetic acid)	Acidity regulator	☺	Regarded as safe in food use; skin and eye irritation; moderate toxicity by ingestion	Foods for infants, raw meats, poultry, game	Cosmetics, textiles, photographic and dye processes

Number	Names	Functions	Code	Potential Effects	Possible Food Use	Other Uses
263	**CALCIUM ACETATE** (by-product in the manufacture of wood alcohol)	Acidity regulator	☺☺	Regarded as safe in food use; low oral toxicity	Foods for infants, processed foods	Cosmetic fragrance, dyeing and tannin skins
264	**AMMONIUM ACETATE** (salt of acetic acid)	Acidity regulator	☹	Nausea; vomiting; carcinogenic	Foods for infants, processed foods	Cosmetics, diuretic
270	**LACTIC ACID** (produced commercially from whey, cornstarch, potatoes and molasses; may be of **ANIMAL** origin; may be **GM**)	Acidity regulator	☺	Regarded as safe in food use. In cosmetics stinging of the skin in sensitive people; not recommended for babies under 3 months	Foods for infants, infant formula products, fruit and vegetable juices, wine, sparkling wine, fruit wines	Cosmetics, skin fresheners, cigarettes
280	**PROPIONIC ACID** (synthetic; obtained from wood pulp, waste liquor or by fermentation)	Preservative	☹	Migraines; skin irritation; headaches; toxic to human cells; toxic to rats in large oral doses; harmful to aquatic organisms	Breads, flour products, bakery products	Perfume bases, cosmetics
281	**SODIUM PROPIONATE** (sodium salt of propionic acid)	Preservative	☹	Behavioural problems; skin irritation; learning difficulties; asthma; gastric irritation; headache; migraines; *see also Calcium Propionate (282)*	Spreads, chutney, jams, breads, flour products, bakery products, sauces, toppings	Cosmetics, medical treatment of fungal infections of the skin

Number	Names	Functions	Code	Potential Effects	Possible Food Use	Other Uses
282	**CALCIUM PROPIONATE** (calcium salt of propionic acid)	Preservative	☹	Irritability; asthma; migraine; fatigue; learning difficulties; aggression; gastric irritation; headaches; sensitivity to propionates occurs in conjunction with sensitivity to other chemicals	Breads, spreads, jams, chutney, flour products, bakery products, sauces, toppings	Cosmetics, antifungal medication
283	**POTASSIUM PROPIONATE** (potassium salt of propionic acid)	Preservative	☹	Asthma; learning difficulties; headache; behavioural problems; migraine; *see also Calcium Propionate (282)*	Bread, biscuits, cakes, pastries and other flour and bakery products	Cosmetics
290	**CARBON DIOXIDE** (commercially produced by fermentation)	Propellant	☺	Probably safe with food use; may reduce fertility; teratogenic; neurotoxicity	Mineral water, wine, sparkling wine, fortified wine, beer, fruit wines	Dry ice, stage 'fog or smoke', cigarettes
296	**MALIC ACID** (from fruit or made synthetically)	Acidity regulator	☺	Regarded as safe in food use; skin & mucous membrane irritation; may aggrevate herpes simplex virus	Wine, sparkling wine, fortified wine, fruit and vegetable juices	Cosmetics, hair laquer, supplements

Number	Names	Functions	Code	Potential Effects	Possible Food Use	Other Uses
297	**FUMARIC ACID** (made by the fermentation of glucose or molasses by fungi)	Acidity regulator	☺☺	Regarded as safe in food use	Wine, sparkling wine, fortified wine, fruit wine	Cosmetics, supplements
300	**ASCORBIC ACID** (Vitamin C)	Antioxidant	☺	Regarded as safe in foods; vitamin C has beneficial health effects; skin rashes, diarrhoea, & painful urination from excessive consumption	Foods for infants, frozen fish, vinegar, beer, wine, uncooked crustacea	Cosmetic creams, hair conditioners, supplements, cigarettes
301	**SODIUM ASCORBATE** (synthetic; sodium salt of ascorbic acid)	Antioxidant	☺☺	Regarded as safe in food use	Foods for infants, frozen fish, vinegar, beer, wine	Cosmetics
302	**CALCIUM ASCORBATE** (prepared from ascorbic acid & calcium carbonate)	Antioxidant	☺☺	Regarded as safe in food use at low levels	Foods for infants, frozen fish, vinegar, beer, wine	
303	**POTASSIUM ASCORBATE** (salt of vitamin C)	Antioxidant	☺☺	Regarded as safe in food use at low levels	Foods for infants, frozen fish, vinegar	
304	**ASCORBYL PALMITATE** (may be of **ANIMAL origin**)	Antioxidant	☺	No known adverse effects in humans; retarded growth and bladder stones in rats	Dried milk, milk powder, cream powder, edible oils and oil emulsions	Cosmetic creams and lotions

Number	Names	Functions	Code	Potential Effects	Possible Food Use	Other Uses
306	**Tocopherols concentrate, mixed** (Vitamin E; obtained from edible vegetable oils; may be **GM**)	Antioxidant	☺☺	Regarded as safe in food use; may be destroyed by freezing	Edible oils and oil emulsions, foods for infants, infant formula products	Baby preparations, deodorants, supplements, cigarettes
307	**Alpha-tocopherol** (form of vitamin E, may be synthetic; may be **GM**)	Antioxidant	☺☺	Regarded as safe in food use; may be destroyed by freezing	Edible oils and oil emulsions, foods for infants	Skin creams and ointments, multi-vitamins
308	**Gamma-tocopherol** (form of vitamin E, synthetic; may be **GM**)	Antioxidant	☺☺	This type of Vitamin E has been shown to play several protective roles in the body	Edible oils and oil emulsions	As part of mixed tocopherol supplements
309	**Delta-tocopherol** (form of vitamin E, synthetic; may be **GM**)	Antioxidant	☺☺	Vitamin E has been shown to play protective roles in the body	Edible oils and oil emulsions	As part of mixed tocopherol supplements
310	**Propyl gallate** (synthetic ester of gallic acid)	Antioxidant	😐?	Asthma; contact dermatitis; gastric irritation; aspirin sensitive people may wish to avoid; not permitted in foods for babies and young children	Edible oils and oil emulsions, bubble gum and chewing gum, preparations of food additives	Cosmetic lotions and creams, surface of labels and tapes applied to foods

Number	Names	Functions	Code	Potential Effects	Possible Food Use	Other Uses
311	**Octyl gallate** (synthetic; salt of gallic acid)	Antioxidant	😐 ?	Mildly toxic by ingestion; allergic reactions; gastric irritation; aspirin sensitive people may wish to avoid	Edible oils and oil emulsions	Cosmetics
312	**Dodecyl gallate** (ester of gallic acid derived from tannin)	Antioxidant	😐 ?	Allergic reactions; NRC; contact dermatitis; gastric irritation; aspirin sensitive people may wish to avoid; caused pathological changes in the spleen, kidneys and liver in test rats	Edible oils and oil emulsions	Cosmetic creams, ink
315	**Erythorbic acid** (an isomer of ascorbic acid; produced from sugar)	Antioxidant	☺	May cause allergic reactions in some people; has only 5% of the vitamin capacity of ascorbic acid	Vinegar, fortified wine, wine, beer, sparkling wine, uncooked crustacea, frozen fish products	Cosmetics
316	**Sodium erythorbate** (sodium salt of erythorbic acid)	Antioxidant	☺	Regarded as safe in food use; has not been studied for mutagenic and teratogenic effects	Fortified wine, wine, sparkling wine, uncooked crustacea, frozen fish products	Cosmetics, water softener, detergent

Number	Names	Functions	Code	Potential Effects	Possible Food Use	Other Uses
319	*tert*-**BUTYLHYDRO-QUINONE** (contains a petroleum derivative, often used with BHA & BHT; banned in some countries)	Antioxidant	☹☹	Moderately toxic by ingestion; birth defects; tinnitus, allergic contact dermatitis; may be carcinogenic and mutagenic	Edible oils and oil emulsions	Suntan lotion, hair colouring, cosmetics
320	**BUTYLATED HYDROXYANISOLE** (BHA; petroleum derivative; banned in some countries)	Antioxidant	☹☹	Hay fever; headache; wheezing; fatigue; asthma; gastrointestinal, liver, endocrine, immuno and neurotoxicity; NRC; carcinogenic	Dried milk, milk powder, cream powder, dried instant mashed potato, bubble gum and chewing gum	Cosmetics, plastic food wrap
321	**BUTYLATED HYDROXYTOLUENE** (BHA; petroleum derivative; banned in some countries)	Antioxidant Preservative	☹☹	Chronic urticaria; dermatitis; fatigue; asthma; aggressive behaviour; learning difficulties; bronchospasm; NRC; may affect kidneys and liver; harmful to aquatic organisms	Edible fats and oils, walnut and pecan nut kernels, bubble gum and chewing gum, polyethylene film for wrapping food	Shaving cream, baby oil, baby lotion, lipsticks, eyeliner, packaging materials, rubber, mastitis treatment in dairy cattle
322	**LECITHIN** (from egg yolk or soya beans; may be **ANIMAL** origin; may be **GE**)	Antioxidant Emulsifier	☺	Regarded as safe in food use; people with allergy to soy may wish to avoid	Foods for infants, infant formula products	Cosmetics, lipsticks, hand creams, pharmaceuticals

Number	Names	Function	Code	Potential Effects	Possible Food Use	Other Uses
325	**SODIUM LACTATE** (sodium salt of lactic acid; may be of **ANIMAL** origin)	Humectant Bulking agent	☺	Regarded as safe in food use; people with lactose intolerance may wish to avoid	Foods for infants, processed foods	Moisturisers, skin and hair products
326	**POTASSIUM LACTATE** (potassium salt of lactic acid; may be of **ANIMAL** origin; may be **GM**)	Acidity regulator Humectant	☺	Regarded as safe in food use; people with lactose intolerance may wish to avoid	Foods for infants, processed foods	Cosmetics
327	**CALCIUM LACTATE** (may be of **ANIMAL** origin)	Acidity regulator	😐?	Regarded as safe in food use; may cause cardiac & gastrointestinal disturbance; people with lactose intolerance may wish to avoid	Foods for infants, processed foods	Oral menstrual drug products? (unsafe), dentifrices, animal feeds
328	**AMMONIUM LACTATE** (may be of **ANIMAL** origin)	Acidity regulator	☺	Regarded as safe in food use; people with lactose intolerance may wish to avoid	Foods for infants, processed foods	Skin conditioner
329	**MAGNESIUM LACTATE** (may be of **ANIMAL** origin)	Acidity regulator	☺	Regarded as safe in food use; people with lactose intolerance may wish to avoid	Cacao products, canned peas	

Number	Names	Functions	Code	Potential Effects	Possible Food Use	Other Uses
330	**CITRIC ACID** (occurs naturally in citrus fruits & berries; produced synthetically; often contains MSG; may be GM)	Acidity regulator Antioxidant	😐 ?	Regarded as safe in foods; has a number of health benefits; may provoke symptoms in those who react to MSG; may aggrevate the herpes simplex virus; in cosmetic use it may cause exfoliative dermatitis; eye and skin irritation	Foods for infants, infant formula products, uncooked crustacea, fruit and vegetable juices, fruit wine, mead, wine, sparkling wine, fortified wine	Shampoos, freckle creams, eye lotions, nail bleaches, skin fresheners, hair rinses, skin bleaching creams
331	**SODIUM CITRATE; SODIUM DIHYDROGEN CITRATE** (salts of citric acid)	Acidity regulator Emulsifier Stabiliser	😐 ?	Can provoke symptoms in those who react to MSG; may alter urinary excretion of some drugs making them either less effective or more potent	Foods for infants, infant formula products, uncooked crustacea	Cosmetics, cigarettes
332	**POTASSIUM CITRATE; POTASSIUM DIHYDROGEN CITRATE** (salts of citric acid)	Acidity regulator Stabiliser	😐 ?	May provoke symptoms in those who react to MSG; may interfere with the results of laboratory tests for pancreatic, blood and liver function	Foods for infants, infant formula products, uncooked crustacea	Urinary alkalizer, gastric antacid

Number	Names	Functions	Code	Potential Effects	Possible Food Use	Other Uses
333	**CALCIUM CITRATE** (prepared from citrus fruits)	Acidity regulator Stabiliser	☺	May provoke symptoms in those who react to MSG; citrates may interfere with the results of laboratory tests for blood, liver and pancreatic function	Confectionery, jellies, jams, to improve baking properties in flour	
334	**TARTARIC ACID** (by-product of the wine industry)	Acidity regulator Antioxidant	☺	Regarded as safe in food use at low levels; excess may have a laxative effect & lower serum lithium levels	Wine, sparkling wine and fortified wine, fruit and vegetable juices, fruit wine, mead	Denture powder, hair rinses, nail bleaches, depilatories
335	**SODIUM TARTRATE** (sodium salt of tartaric acid)	Acidity regulator	☺☺	Regarded as safe in food use	Fruit and vegetable juices	
336	**POTASSIUM TARTRATE OR POTASSIUM ACID TARTRATE** (potassium salt of tartaric acid)	Acidity regulator Stabiliser	😐?	Should be avoided by people with impaired kidney or liver function; high blood pressure; oedema or cardiac failure	Wine, sparkling wine and fortified wine, fruit and vegetable juices	

Number	Names	Functions	Code	Potential Effects	Possible Food Use	Other Uses
337	**Potassium sodium tartrate** (sodium and potassium salt of tartaric acid; Rochelle salt)	Acidity regulator Stabiliser	☺	People with oedema, high blood pressure, cardiac failure, kidney or liver damage advised to avoid	Fruit and vegetable juices, wine, sparkling wine and fortified wine	Silvering of mirrors, mouthwash, cathartic in medicinal use
338	**Phosphoric acid** (made from phosphate rock)	Acidity regulator	😐 ?	Regarded as safe in food use at low levels; excess may lead to tooth erosion and calcium loss in bones	Cheese products, kola type drinks, jellies, sweets	Cigarettes, hair tonic, nail polish, metal polish
339	**Sodium phosphate** (salt of phosphoric acid)	Acidity regulator Emulsifier	☺	Regarded as safe in foods at low levels; contact can cause skin irritation; erythema; blisters	Frozen fish products	Manufacture of nail enamels and detergents
340	**Potassium phosphate** (salt of phosphoric acid)	Acidity regulator Stabiliser	☺☺	Regarded as safe in food use	Frozen fish products	Shampoo, cuticle remover
341	**Calcium phosphate** (salt of phosphoric acid)	Emulsifier Stabiliser	☺	Regarded as safe in foods; can cause skin & eye irritation on contact	Fruit wine, frozen fish products, salt and salt substitutes	Toothpaste, tooth powder, cosmetics
342	**Ammonium phosphate** (salt of phosphoric acid)	Mineral salt Buffer	☺	Thought to be safe; has a diuretic effect; makes urine more acidic	Flour products, canned fish	Mouthwash, fireproofing agent

Number	Names	Functions	Code	Potential Effects	Possible Food Use	Other Uses
343	**MAGNESIUM PHOSPHATE**	Anticaking agent	☺☺	Regarded as safe in food use	Dried milk, milk powder	
349	**AMMONIUM MALATE** (salt of malic acid)	Acidity regulator	☺☺	Regarded as safe in food use	Processed foods	
350	**SODIUM MALATE** (sodium salt of malic acid)	Acidity regulator Humectant	☺☺	Regarded as safe in food use	Fruit drink, soft drink, sweetened coconut	Anti-aging products
351	**POTASSIUM MALATE** (potassium salt of malic acid)	Acidity regulator	☺☺	Regarded as safe in food use	Fruit drinks, soft drinks, sweetened coconut	Tobacco, matches
352	**CALCIUM MALATE** (calcium salt of malic acid)	Acidity regulator	☺☺	Regarded as safe in food use	Fruit drinks, soft drink, sweetened coconut	
353	**METATARTARIC ACID** (from tartaric acid)	Acidity regulator	☺	Regarded as safe in food use at low levels; *see Tartaric Acid (334)*	Wine, sparkling wine, fruit and vegetable juices	
354	**CALCIUM TARTRATE** (derived from cream of tartar)	Acidity regulator	☺☺	Regarded as safe in food use	Fruit and vegetable juices	Tobacco

Number	Names	Functions	Code	Potential Effects	Possible Food Use	Other Uses
355	**ADIPIC ACID** (prepared from the oxidation of cyclohexanol by nitric acid with the liberation of nitrous oxide, a greenhouse gas)	Acidity regulator	😐 ?	Regarded as safe in food use at low levels; moderately toxic by ingestion; toxic effects in rats including death; teratogenic	Beverages, baked goods, oils, snack foods, processed cheese	Manufacture of plastics and nylons
357	**POTASSIUM ADIPATE** (salt of adipic acid)	Acidity regulator	☺ ☺	Regarded as safe in food use at low levels	Low-sodium salt substitutes	Boiler water
359	**AMMONIUM ADIPATES** (salts of adipic acid)	Acidity regulator	☺ ☺	Regarded as safe in food use at low levels	Salt substitute	
363	**SUCCINIC ACID** (synthetic; made from acetic acid)	Acidity regulator	☺	Regarded as safe in food use at low levels; excess can cause vomiting and diarrhoea	Salt substitute	Sports formulas, inks, perfumes, lacquers, paint, mouthwash
365	**SODIUM FUMARATE** (salt of fumaric acid)	Acidity regulator	☺ ☺	Regarded as safe in food use	Fruit juice, jelly, pie filling, cheese, marmalade, jam	
366	**POTASSIUM FUMARATE** (salt of fumaric acid)	Acidity regulator	☺ ☺	Regarded as safe in food use	Fruit juice, jelly, pie filling, cheese, marmalade, jam	

Number	Names	Functions	Code	Potential Effects	Possible Food Use	Other Uses
367	**Calcium fumarate** (salt of fumaric acid)	Acidity regulator	☺☺	Regarded as safe in food use	Fruit juice, jelly, pie filling, cheese, marmalade, jam	
368	**Ammonium fumarate** (salt of fumaric acid)	Acidity regulator	☺☺	Regarded as safe in food use	Processed foods	
380	**Ammonium citrate; triammonium citrate**	Acidity regulator	☺	May provoke symptoms in those who react to MSG	Foods for infants, uncooked crustacea	
381	**Ferric ammonium citrate**	Acidity regulator	☺☺	Regarded as safe in food use	Salts and condiments	Dietary iron supplements
385	**Calcium disodium ethylenediaminetetra-acetate or calcium disodium EDTA** (banned in some countries)	Preservative Antioxidant	☹	Muscle cramps; blood in the urine; intestinal upset; kidney damage; chromosome damage; can increase uptake of heavy metals; may affect liver & reproduction	Canned fish products, fruit drinks, flavoured drinks, sauces and toppings	Medicinally to detoxify heavy metal poisoning
400	**Alginic acid** (seaweed extract; may contain fluoride)	Thickener Stabiliser	☺	Safe in foods at low levels; alginates inhibited absorption of essential nutrients in some animal tests	Ice cream, dessert mix, custard mix, flavoured milk, cordials, infant formula, yoghurt	Sizing paper and textiles, cosmetics

Number	Names	Functions	Code	Potential Effects	Possible Food Use	Other Uses
401	**SODIUM ALGINATE** (sodium salt of alginic acid)	Thickener Stabiliser Emulsifier	☺	Alginates may have beneficial health effects; alginates inhibited absorption of essential nutrients in animal tests	Frozen desserts, jams, fruit jelly preserves	Baby lotions, wave sets, manufacture of cosmetics
402	**POTASSIUM ALGINATE** (potassium salt of alginic acid)	Thickener Stabiliser	☺	Alginates may have beneficial effects on health; alginates inhibited absorption of essential nutrients in some animal tests	Ice cream, yoghurt, custard mix	Shampoo, hand lotion, wave sets and lotions
403	**AMMONIUM ALGINATE** (ammonium salt of alginic acid)	Thickener Stabiliser	☺	Alginates may have beneficial effects on health; alginates inhibit absorption of essential nutrients in animal tests	Dessert mix, custard mix, ice cream, yoghurt	Cosmetics; boiler water
404	**CALCIUM ALGINATE** (calcium salt of alginic acid)	Thickener Stabiliser Gelling agent	☺	Alginates may have beneficial effects on health; they inhibited absorption of essential nutrients in animal tests	Ice cream, soft and cottage cheeses, cheese snacks, instant desserts	Hand lotions and creams, shampoos, wave sets

Number	Names	Functions	Code	Potential Effects	Possible Food Use	Other Uses
405	**PROPYLENE GLYCOL ALGINATE** (synthetic; ester of alginic acid from brown seaweeds)	Thickener Emulsifier	😐 ?	Can cause allergic reactions; reduced growth and loose stools in animal studies; alginates inhibited absorption of essential nutrients in some animal tests	Beer and related products	Stabiliser and defoamer in cosmetics
406	**AGAR** (derived from red algae)	Thickener Stabilizer Gelling agent	😊	Regarded as safe in foods at low levels; excess may cause intestinal obstruction and flatulence	Ice cream, baked goods, desserts, manufactured meats, jellies	Emulsifier and emollient in cosmetics, bulk laxative
407	**CARRAGEENAN** (may be degraded, undegraded or native; may contain or create MSG)	Thickener Stabilizer Gelling agent	☹	May affect gastrointestinal tract; stomach; NRC; ulcerative colitis; animal carcinogen	Foods for infants, liquid infant formula products	Cosmetics, cough medicines, toothpaste
407a	**PROCESSED EUCHEUMA SEAWEED**	Thickener Stabilizer	😐 ?	Uncertainties exist as to this additive's safety	Processed foods	Skin conditioner
409	**ARABINOGALACTAN OR LARCH GUM** (extracted from larch wood; contains high levels of tannic acid)	Thickener Stabilizer Gelling agent	😐 ?	Claimed to have beneficial health effects; may cause allergic reactions; tannic acid is thought to be a weak carcinogen	Processed foods	Essential oils

Number	Names	Functions	Code	Potential Effects	Possible Food Use	Other Uses
410	**LOCUST BEAN GUM OR CAROB BEAN GUM** (from the carob tree)	Thickener Stabiliser	☺☺	Regarded as safe in food use; may have beneficial health effects	Infant formula products, foods for infants	Cosmetics, animal feed, detergent,
412	**GUAR GUM** (obtained from the seeds of a tree in India)	Thickener Stabiliser	☺	Regarded as safe in foods at low levels; may have beneficial health effects; excess can lead to abdominal cramps & obstruction, flatulence, nausea & diarrhoea	Infant formula products, foods for infants	Binding tablets, cosmetics, slimming aids (caution advised)
413	**TRAGACANTH GUM** (derived from astragalus gummifer, a plant found in the Middle East)	Thickener Stabiliser	😐?	Regarded as safe in food use at low levels; adverse reactions such as asthma, abdominal pain, contact dermatitis, dyspnoea, anaphylaxis and constipation can occur but are rare	Sauces, fruit jelly, salad dressing, confections, icings	Shaving cream, rouge, toothpaste, foundation
414	**ACACIA OR GUM ARABIC** (extracted from acacia Senegal)	Thickener Stabiliser	😐?	Low oral toxicity; may cause skin rash & provoke asthma attack; may interfere with the absorption of oral medications	Foods for infants, wine, sparkling wine, fortified wine	Cosmetics, hair products, medicines

Number	Names	Functions	Code	Potential Effects	Possible Food Use	Other Uses
415	**XANTHAN GUM** (made by the fermentation of a carbohydrate with a bacterium; may be **GM**)	Thickener Emulsifier	☺☺	Regarded as safe in food use	Jellies, sweets, dairy products, breakfast cereal, salad dressing	Toothpaste, deodorant, cosmetics, cigarettes
416	**KARAYA GUM** (exudate of a tree found in India)	Thickener Stabilizer	☹	Asthma; urticaria; hay fever; dermatitis; reduces nutrient intake; gastric irritation	Ice cream, baked goods, sweets, gumdrops, frozen dairy desserts	Hair sprays, hand lotions, toothpaste, shaving creams
418	**GELLAN GUM** (gum made by the fermentation of a carbohydrate with *pseudomonas elodea*)	Thickener Stabilizer	☺	Regarded as safe in food use at low levels; excess can cause diarrhoea	Processed foods	Cosmetics
420	**SORBITOL OR SORBITOL SYRUP** (may be synthesised from glucose)	Humectant Sweetener Emulsifier	😐?	Excess intake can cause intestinal cramps; diarrhoea; gastrointestinal disturbance; may alter absorption of drugs so they are either more toxic or less effective	Confectionery, dried fruit, chewing gum, chocolate, lollies	Cosmetics, hair spray, shampoos, mouthwash, toothpaste, embalming fluid, antifreeze
421	**MANNITOL** (manufactured synthetically)	Humectant Sweetener	☹	Hypersensitivity reactions; nausea; vomiting; diarrhoea; urticaria; NRC & diabetics; kidney dysfunction; anaphylaxis	Carbohydrate modified foods or low calorie foods, chewing gum, jam, confectionery	Hand cream and lotion, hair grooming products

Number	Names	Functions	Code	Potential Effects	Possible Food Use	Other Uses
422	**GLYCERIN OR GLYCEROL** (synthetic; by-product of soap manufacture or by synthesis of propylene; may be of **ANIMAL** origin)	Humectant Solvent Emollient	☺	Regarded as safe in food use at low levels; mental confusion; headache; may affect stomach, heart, reproduction, blood sugar levels	Confectionery, dried fruit, low calorie foods, marshmallows, baked goods, chewing gum	Tobacco, soap, toothpaste, hand cream, mouthwash, barrier cream, perfumery
431	**POLYOXYETHYLENE** (40) **STEARATE** (may be of **ANIMAL** origin)	Emulsifier	😐?	Skin tumours in mice; may facilitate the penetration of cancer-causing additives	Dried milk, milk powder, cream powder, wine, sparkling wine	Hand creams and lotions
433	**POLYSORBATE** 80 **OR POLYOXYETHYLENE** (20) **SORBITAN MONOOLEATE** (may be of **ANIMAL** origin)	Emulsifier	☹	Associated with the contaminants 1,4 dioxane & ethylene oxide which cause cancer in animals	Icing, frozen custard, sherbet, spiced green beans, pickles	Baby lotion, suntan lotion, bath oils
435	**POLYSORBATE** 60 **OR POLYOXYETHYLENE** (20) **SORBITAN MONOSTEARATE** (may be of **ANIMAL** origin)	Emulsifier	☹	*See Polysorbate 80 (433) and 1,4 Dioxane and Ethylene Oxide in section 2*	Cakes, cake mixes, icing, confectionery, beverage mixes	Topical treatment for hair loss in men
436	**POLYSORBATE** 65 **OR POLYOXYETHYLENE** (20) **SORBITAN TRISTEARATE** (may be of **ANIMAL** origin)	Emulsifier	☹	Polysorbates can contain residues of harmful chemicals; can increase the absorption of fat soluble substances	Ice cream, frozen custard, cake icings and fillings	

Number	Names	Functions	Code	Potential Effects	Possible Food Use	Other Uses
440	**PECTIN** (from apple residue and orange pith)	Stabiliser Thickener Gelling agent	☺	May provoke symptoms in those who react to MSG; may have beneficial health effects	Foods for infants	Toothpaste, antidiarrheal medicines, hair-setting lotion
442	**AMMONIUM SALTS OF PHOSPHATIDIC ACID** (may be synthetic; may be of **ANIMAL** origin)	Emulsifier	☺☺	Regarded as safe in food use	Bread, chocolate, confectionery, frying oils	
444	**SUCROSE ACETATE ISOBUTYRATE** (made from sucrose)	Emulsifier Stabiliser	☺	Regarded as safe in foods; produced liver damage in dogs but not in other species	Fruit drinks, flavoured drinks, sauces and toppings	Denaturant for rubbing alcohol
445	**GLYCEROL ESTERS OF WOOD ROSINS** (made from wood rosin and food grade glycerin; may be of **ANIMAL** origin)	Emulsifier Stabiliser	😐?	Not granted GRAS status in the USA due to insufficient safety data	Fruit drinks, flavoured drinks, sauces and toppings	
450	**POTASSIUM PYROPHOSPHATE; SODIUM ACID PYROPHOSPHATE; SODIUM PYROPHOSPHATE**	Emulsifier Stabiliser Acidity regulator	☺	Regarded as safe in food use at low levels; excess may cause kidney damage, decrease in bone density; osteoporosis	Frozen fish products	

Number	Names	Functions	Code	Potential Effects	Possible Food Use	Other Uses
451	**POTASSIUM TRIPOLYPHOSPHATE; SODIUM TRIPOLYPHOSPHATE** (made synthetically from phosphate rock)	Acidity regulator	☺	Regarded as safe in food use; can be irritating to skin and mucous membranes	Frozen fish products	Bubble bath, soap
452	**POTASSIUM POLYMETAPHOSPHATE; SODIUM METAPHOSPHATE; INSOLUBLE; SODIUM POLYPHOSPHATES, GLASSY** (salts of phosphoric acid)	Emulsifier Stabiliser	☺	Regarded as safe in food use; may cause digestive disturbance; can be irritating to skin and mucous membranes	Frozen fish products	Fertilisers, detergents
460	**CELLULOSE MICROCRYSTALLINE; CELLULOSE, POWDERED** (prepared from wood pulp; may be **GM**)	Anticaking agent Binder	☺☺	Regarded as safe in food use; may have beneficial health effects	Cakes, sauces, soups, biscuits, bread, spreads and jams, ice cream	Cosmetic creams, tablets
461	**METHYL CELLULOSE** (made from wood pulp or chemical cotton; may be **GM**)	Thickener Stabiliser Emulsifier	☺	Regarded as safe in food use at low levels; laxative effect with excess	Infant formula, ice cream, toppings, confectionery, imitation fruit, soup	Cosmetics, sun creams, slimming aids, hand creams & lotions
463	**HYDROXYPROPYL CELLULOSE** (synthetic ether of cellulose; may be **GM**)	Thickener Emulsifier Stabiliser	☺	Regarded as safe in food use; may cause allergic reactions	Low fat cream, UHT cream	Cosmetics, hair products, tobacco

Number	Names	Functions	Code	Potential Effects	Possible Food Use	Other Uses
464	**HYDROXYPROPYL METHYLCELLULOSE** (synthetic; from cellulose; may be **GM**)	Thickener Emulsifier Stabiliser	☺	Regarded as safe in food use; mild eye and skin irritation; allergic reactions	Confectionery, infant formula, icing, topping, ice cream, imitation fruit	Hair and skin preparations, bubble baths, tanning lotions
465	**METHYL ETHYL CELLULOSE** (from wood pulp or chemical cotton)	Thickener Emulsifier Stabiliser	😐 ?	Can cause digestive problems; diarrhoea; flatulence; gastrointest-inal disturbances	Vegetable fat, low fat cream, imitation ice cream, whipped toppings	Bulk laxative, tobacco
466	**SODIUM CARBOXY-METHYLCELLULOSE** (made from cotton by-products; may be **GM**)	Thickener Stabiliser	😐 ?	Poorly absorbed; flat-ulence; large amounts can cause diarrhoea and abdominal cramps; caused cancer & tum-ours in animal studies	Infant formula, ice cream, icings, confectionery, cottage cheese, cream cheese spread	Hair setting lotions, hand cream, drugs, laxatives, antacids, tobacco
470	**ALUMINIUM, CALCIUM, SODIUM, MAGNESIUM, POTASSIUM & AMMONIUM SALTS OF FATTY ACIDS** (may be of **ANIMAL** origin)	Stabiliser Emulsifier Anticaking agent	☺☺	Regarded as safe in food use	Cake mixes, oven ready chips	
471	**MONO- & DI-GLYCERIDES OF FATTY ACIDS** (may be of **ANIMAL** origin; may be **GM**)	Stabiliser Emulsifier	☺☺	Regarded as safe in food use	Foods for infants, cereals and cereal products	

Number	Names	Functions	Code	Potential Effects	Possible Food Use	Other Uses
472a	**ACETIC AND FATTY ACID ESTERS OF GLYCEROL** (may be of **ANIMAL** origin; may be **GM**)	Emulsifier Stabiliser	☺☺	Regarded as safe in food use	Confectionery, ice cream, bread, dessert toppings, cheesecake mix	
472b	**LACTIC AND FATTY ACID ESTERS OF GLYCEROL** (may be of **ANIMAL** origin)	Emulsifier Stabiliser	☺☺	Regarded as safe in food use	Bakery products, peanut butter, whipped toppings	
472c	**CITRIC AND FATTY ACID ESTERS OF GLYCEROL** (may be of **ANIMAL** origin)	Emulsifier Stabiliser	☺	May provoke symptoms in those who react to MSG	Infant formula products for specific dietary use	
472e	**DIACETYLTARTARIC AND FATTY ACID ESTERS OF GLYCEROL** (may be of **ANIMAL** origin)	Emulsifier	☺☺	Regarded as safe in food use	Infant formula products for specific dietary use	Cosmetic creams
472f	**MIXED TARTARIC, ACETIC AND FATTY ACID ESTERS OF GLYCEROL OR TARTARIC, ACETIC & FATTY ACID ESTERS OF GLYCEROL (MIXED)** (may be of **ANIMAL** origin)	Emulsifier Stabiliser	☺☺	Regarded as safe in food use	Processed bread	Cosmetic creams

Number	Names	Functions	Code	Potential Effects	Possible Food Use	Other Uses
473	**SUCROSE ESTERS OF FATTY ACIDS** (from sucrose and fatty acids, may be of **ANIMAL** origin; may be **GM**)	Emulsifier	☺	Regarded as safe in foods at low levels; large doses can cause nausea, diarrhoea, gas, bloating, abdominal pain; can facilitate uptake of food allergens	Surface treated fruits and vegetables	
475	**POLYGLYCEROL ESTERS OF FATTY ACIDS** (may be of **ANIMAL** origin; may be **GM**)	Emulsifier	☺☺	Regarded as safe in food use	Whipped thickened light cream, edible oils, margarine, biscuits, cakes	
476	**POLYGLYCEROL ESTERS OF INTERESTERIFIED RICINOLEIC ACID** (from castor oil & glycerol esters; may be of **ANIMAL** origin; may be **GM**)	Emulsifier	☺☺	Regarded as safe in food use	Dairy and fat based desserts, dips and snacks, margarine, edible oils, chocolate and cocoa products	
477	**PROPYLENE GLYCOL MONO- AND DIESTERS OR PROPYLENE GLYCOL ESTERS OF FATTY ACIDS** (may be of **ANIMAL** origin; may be **GM**)	Emulsifier	☺☺	Regarded as safe in food use	Chocolate and cocoa products	

Number	Names	Functions	Code	Potential Effects	Possible Food Use	Other Uses
480	**DIOCTYL SODIUM SULPHOSUCCINATE**	Emulsifier	😐 ?	Undergoing further evaluation for safety	Sauces, fruit drinks, flavoured drinks	Laxatives, cosmetics
481	**SODIUM LACTYLATE**; **SODIUM OLEYL LACTYLATE**; **SODIUM STEAROYL LACTYLATE** (from lactic acid and fatty acids; may be of **ANIMAL** origin; may be **GM**)	Emulsifier Stabiliser	☺ ☺	Regarded as safe in food use at low levels	Biscuits, bread, cakes, cake icings, fillings and toppings	
482	**CALCIUM LACTYLATE**; **CALCIUM OLEYL LACTYLATE**; **CALCIUM STEAROYL LACTYLATE** (calcium salt of lactyl lactate; may be of **ANIMAL** origin)	Emulsifier Stabiliser	☺	Regarded as safe in food use; adverse reactions have occurred in animals during testing	Flour for making bread, biscuits, instant mashed potatoes, processed egg whites	Powdered cosmetics
491	**SORBITAN MONOSTEARATE** (synthesised from sorbitol and stearic acid; may be of **ANIMAL** origin; may be **GM**)	Emulsifier	☺	Regarded as safe in food use at low levels; high dietary levels can cause intralobular fibrosis; growth retardation; liver enlargement	Fruit wine, mead, vegetable wine, wine, sparkling wine and fortified wine	Cosmetic creams and lotions, suntan creams, skin creams, deodorants

Number	Names	Functions	Code	Potential Effects	Possible Food Use	Other Uses
492	**SORBITAN TRISTEARATE** (prepared from sorbitol and stearic acid; may be of **ANIMAL** origin; may be **GM**)	Emulsifier	☺	Regarded as safe in food use at low levels; high dietary levels can cause intralobular fibrosis; growth retardation; liver enlargement	Compounded chocolate, oil toppings, cake mixes	Pharmceuticals, cosmetic creams, nail strengthening cream
500	**SODIUM CARBONATE**; **SODIUM BICARBONATE** (baking soda, bicarbonate of soda; mostly made synthetically)	Acidity regulator Anticaking agent Raising agent	😐?	Regarded as safe in food use at low levels; contact can cause forehead, scalp and hand rash; respiratory distress; large doses can cause gastrointestinal bleeding, vomiting, diarrhoea and shock	Uncooked crustacea, foods for infants, fruit wine, mead, vegetable wine	Mouthwash, soaps, bath salts, vaginal douches, shampoos, laundry detergent, paper and glass manufacture
501	**POTASSIUM CARBONATE**; **POTASSIUM BICARBONATE** (inorganic salt of potassium)	Acidity regulator Stabiliser	😐?	Regarded as safe in foods; dermatitis of the hands, forehead, scalp; eye irritation; upper respiratory tract irritation	Foods for infants, wines, fruit wine, mead, vegetable wine	Shampoos, permanent wave lotions, washing powder
503	**AMMONIUM BICARBONATE**; **AMMONIUM HYDROGEN CARBONATE**	Acidity regulator Raising agent	☺	Regarded as safe in foods; contact can cause rashes on scalp, forehead and hands	Foods for infants, fruit wine, mead, vegetable wine	Permanent wave solutions and creams, fire extinguishers

Number	Names	Functions	Code	Potential Effects	Possible Food Use	Other Uses
504	**MAGNESIUM CARBONATE** (synthetic; from magnesium sulphate and sodium carbonate)	Anticaking agent Acidity regulator	☺	Regarded as safe in food use; excess may have a laxative effect; irritation if applied to abraded skin.	Salts and condiments, uncooked crustacea	Baby powder, face powder, perfume carrier, ink, paint
507	**HYDROCHLORIC ACID** (made from sulphuric acid and sodium chloride)	Acidity regulator	☺☺	Regarded as safe in food use	Cottage cheese, cream cheese	Hair bleach, solvents
508	**POTASSIUM CHLORIDE** (found naturally as sylvite deposites)	Gelling agent	😐?	Regarded as safe in food use at low levels; intestinal ulcers; NRC; cardiovascular, liver and respiratory toxicity	Butter	Cosmetics, fertiliser, pharmaceuticals
509	**CALCIUM CHLORIDE** (chloride salt of calcium)	Firming agent	☺	Regarded as safe in food use; excess can cause stomach upsets; irregular heartbeat	Foods for infants	Cosmetics, antiseptic eye lotions, fire extinguishers
510	**AMMONIUM CHLORIDE** (naturally occuring ammonium salt)	Bulking agent	😐?	Ingestion can cause nausea, headache, acidosis, insomnia and weight loss; contact can cause dermatitis; skin and eye irritation	Flour products, bread, rolls, buns etc, low-sodium dietary foods	Skin wash, eye lotion,shampoo, permanent wave solution, batteries, dyes

Number	Names	Functions	Code	Potential Effects	Possible Food Use	Other Uses
511	**MAGNESIUM CHLORIDE** (synthetic; from hydro-chloric acid & magnesium oxide/hydroxide)	Firming agent	☺	Regarded as safe in food use at low levels; excess may have a laxative effect	Infant formula, salt substitute	Shampoos
512	**STANNOUS CHLORIDE** (a salt of tin)	Antioxidant	😐?	Low systemic toxicity, but may be irritating to skin and mucous membranes; harmful to aquatic organisms	Canned asparagus	Used in the manufacture of dyes
514	**SODIUM SULPHATE** (sodium salt of sulphuric acid)	Acidity regulator	😐?	Regarded as safe in foods at low levels; skin irritation; gastrointestinal irritation; people with poor kidney or liver function should avoid	Chewing gum base, tuna fish, biscuits	Manufacture of dyes, soaps, detergents, glass and paper
515	**POTASSIUM SULPHATE** (naturally occurring mineral)	Acidity regulator	☺	Regarded as safe in food use; large doses cause severe gastro-intestinal bleeding	Soft drinks, brewing industry	Cosmetics, medicines
516	**CALCIUM SULPHATE** (becomes Plaster of Paris when heated)	Firming agent	☺	Regarded as safe in foods; large amounts may cause intestinal obstruction, constipation	Fruit wines, mead, vegetable wines	Toothpaste, tooth powder, cosmetics

Number	Names	Functions	Code	Potential Effects	Possible Food Use	Other Uses
518	**MAGNESIUM SULPHATE** (epsom salts is a form of hydrated magnesium sulphate)	Firming agent	😐 ?	May cause magnesium poisoning in those who have impaired kidney function	Infant formula as a nutrient additive, brewing beer	Laxative, fire-proofing fabrics, fertiliser
519	**CUPRIC SULPHATE** (soluble salt of copper)	Mineral salt	☹	Gastrointestinal, liver, kidney, cardiovascular and neurotoxicity; skin and mucous membrane irritation; very toxic to aquatic organisms	Infant formula	Hair dyes, fungicide, herbicide, preparation of azo dyes
526	**CALCIUM HYDROXIDE** (slaked lime)	Acidity regulator Firming agent	☺	Regarded as safe in food use; toxic and hazardous in concentrated form	Infant formula products	Depilatories, animal feeds, plaster, pesticides
529	**CALCIUM OXIDE** (quick lime; strongly caustic)	Acidity regulator	😐 ?	Regarded as safe in food use; can cause severe damage to skin & mucous membranes on contact; thermal and chemical burns	Confectionery, ice cream mix, canned peas, custard mix, malted milk powder	Bath products, hair bleach, home & garden pesticides, insecticides
530	**MAGNESIUM OXIDE** (from magnesite ores)	Anticaking agent	☺ ☺	Regarded as safe in food use	Dried milk, milk and cream powder	

Number	Names	Functions	Code	Potential Effects	Possible Food Use	Other Uses
535	**Sodium ferrocyanide** (synthetic; from the reaction of cyanide with iron sulphate)	Anticaking agent	☺☺	Regarded as safe in food use	Salts and condiments	Processing aid in wine
536	**Potassium ferrocyanide** (by-product in purification of coal gas)	Anticaking agent	😐?	Kidney toxicity; skin irritation; may be harmful by inhalation, ingestion and skin absorption; may cause irritation	Salts and condiments	White and rose wine production
541	**Sodium aluminium phosphate**	Emulsifier Acidity regulator	😐?	Regarded as safe in food use at low levels?; people with kidney or heart disease may wish to avoid or limit intake; *see Aluminium (173)*	Baking compounds, cheese spread, processed cheese	
542	**Bone phosphate** (of **animal** origin)	Anticaking agent Emulsifier	☺☺	Regarded as safe in food use	Dried milk, milk powder, cream powder	Filler in tablets
551	**Silicon dioxide, amorphous** (silica; salt from silicic acid)	Anticaking agent	☺☺	Regarded as safe in food use; regarded as having many beneficial health effects	Salts and condiments, dried egg products, beverage whitener	Beer production, animal feed, paper and paperboard

Number	Names	Functions	Code	Potential Effects	Possible Food Use	Other Uses
552	**CALCIUM SILICATE** (made from lime and diatomaceous earth)	Anticaking agent	☺	Practically nontoxic when ingested; inhalation may cause respiratory tract irritation; asthma	Baking powder, rice, chewing gum, salts and condiments	Antacid, face powder, lime glass, cement
553	**MAGNESIUM SILICATE OR TALC** (naturally occurring mineral)	Anticaking agent	☹	Cancers (stomach and ovarian); cough; vomiting; respiratory problems; tumours; stomach problems	Chocolate, chewing gum base, condiments, confectionery, polished rice	Eye shadow, bath powder, baby powder, vitamin supplements
554	**SODIUM ALUMINOSILICATE**	Anticaking agent	😐?	Regarded as safe in food use at low levels?; *see Aluminium (173)*	Salts and condiments	Barrier creams, depilatories
555	**POTASSIUM ALUMINIUM SILICATE**	Anticaking agent	😐?	Regarded as safe in food use at low levels?; *see Aluminium (173)*	Cheese and cheese products, dried milk, milk powder	
556	**CALCIUM ALUMINIUM SILICATE**	Anticaking agent	😐?	Regarded as safe in food use at low levels?; *see Aluminium (173)*	Garlic salt, table salt, vanilla powder	

Number	Names	Functions	Code	Potential Effects	Possible Food Use	Other Uses
558	**BENTONITE** (colloidal white clay)	Anticaking agent Thickener	😐 ?	Regarded as safe in foods; may clog skin pores inhibiting proper skin function; venous injection causes blood clots & possibly tumours	Colouring in wine, sugar brewing and purification, settling wine sediments	Cosmetics, facial masks, animal and poultry feeds, detergents
559	**ALUMINIUM SILICATE** (kaolin)	Anticaking agent	😐 ?	Regarded as safe in food use?; *see Aluminium (173)*	Beer production	Baby powder, bath powder, face powder
560	**POTASSIUM SILICATE** (soluble potash glass)	Anticaking agent Binder	☺ ☺	Regarded as safe in food use	Cheese and cheese products, unripened cheese	Cosmetics, soap manufacture, detergents
570	**STEARIC ACID OR FATTY ACID** (usually from cottonseed oil; may be of **ANIMAL** origin; likely to be **GM**)	Foaming agent Glazing agent	😐 ?	Regarded as safe in food use; contact may cause skin irritation; may cause allergic reactions; needs further study	Essences, soft drinks, artificial sweeteners, fruit flavoured drinks	Bar soaps, lip-sticks, bubble baths, lubricants, detergent
575	**GLUCONO DELTA - LACTONE** (made from the oxidation of glucose; may be **GM**)	Acidity regulator Raising agent	☺	Regarded as safe in food use at low levels; excess can cause diarrhoea	Cottage cheese, meat processing, jelly powder, cann-ed vegetables	Cleaning agents, brewing beer

Number	Names	Functions	Code	Potential Effects	Possible Food Use	Other Uses
577	**POTASSIUM GLUCONATE** (potassium salt of gluconic acid; may be **GM**)	Sequestrant Buffer	☺ ☺	Regarded as safe in food use	Soda water	
578	**CALCIUM GLUCONATE** (calcium salt of gluconic acid; may be **GM**)	Buffer Sequestrant	😐 ?	Gastric irritation; stomach problems, heart problems	Preserves, infant formula, anticaking of coffee powder	Cosmetics, animal feeds
579	**FERROUS GLUCONATE** (made from barium gluconate and ferrous sulphate; may be **GM**)	Colour retention agent Flavouring	☹	Toxic in large amounts; diarrhoea; vomiting; may affect gastrointestinal tract, liver, stomach; caused tumours in mice	Infant formula, formula dietary food, preserved ripe olives	Iron supplements
580	**MAGNESIUM GLUCONATE** (salt of gluconic acid)	Acidity regulator	☺ ☺	Regarded as safe in food use	Soda water	
586	**4-HEXYLRESORCINOL** (resorcinol is obtained from various resins)	Antioxidant	☹	Can cause severe gastrointestinal irritation; bowel, liver and heart damage	Uncooked crustacea	Mouthwash, sunburn cream
620	**L-GLUTAMIC ACID** (synthetically made from vegetable protein; contains MSG; may be **GM**)	Flavour enhancer	😐 ?	Regarded as safe in food use at low levels; excessive amounts may lead to serious health conditions	Adding meat flavour to foods, improving the taste of beer (together with hydrochloric acid)	Cosmetics, permanent wave solutions, treatment of epilepsy

Number	Names	Functions	Code	Potential Effects	Possible Food Use	Other Uses
621	**MONOSODIUM L-GLUTAMATE** (MSG; monosodium salt of glutamic acid; may be **GM**)	Flavour enhancer	☹	Bronchospasm; heart palpitations; abdominal discomfort; irritability; fibromyalgia; nausea; depression; headache; migraine; asthma; blurred vision; vertigo; sight impairment; teratogenic; aspirin sensitive people may wish to avoid; NRC	May be found in packet soup, quick soup, flavoured noodles, textured protein, TVP, malt extract, gelatine, yeast extract, soy sauce, flavourings (chicken, beef, pork, smoke)	Hidden sources of MSG including soap, cosmetics, shampoo, hair conditioner, most 'live virus' vaccines
622	**MONOPOTASSIUM L-GLUTAMATE** (made synthetically; may be **GM**)	Flavour enhancer	☹	*See Monosodium Glutamate (621)*	Meats, low-sodium salt substitute	
623	**CALCIUM GLUTAMATE** (calcium salt of glutamic acid; contains MSG; may be **GM**)	Flavour enhancer	😐?	Asthma; aspirin sensitive people may wish to avoid; probably similar to MSG	Low-sodium salt substitute	
624	**MONOAMMONIUM L-GLUTAMATE** (from glutamic acid; contains MSG; may be **GM**)	Flavour enhancer	😐?	Contains MSG; allergic reactions	Low-sodium salt substitute	

Number	Names	Functions	Code	Potential Effects	Possible Food Use	Other Uses
625	**MAGNESIUM GLUTAMATE** (contains MSG; may be **GM**)	Flavour enhancer	☺	Regarded as safe in food use at low levels; contains MSG; laxative effect with excess	Low sodium salt substitute	
627	**DISODIUM** 5'-**GUANYLATE** (isolated from sardines or yeast extract; often used in combination with MSG; may be of **ANIMAL** origin)	Flavour enhancer	😐?	Aspirin sensitive people may wish to avoid; people with gout or uric acid kidney stones may wish to avoid or limit intake; NRC	Canned foods, sauces, snack foods, soups	
631	**DISODIUM** 5'-**INOSINATE** (of **ANIMAL** origin; often contains MSG)	Flavour enhancer	😐?	People with gout or uric acid kidney stones may wish to avoid; kidney problems; NRC	Canned vegetables	
635	**DISODIUM** 5'-**RIBONUCLEOTIDES** (may be of **ANIMAL** origin; banned in some countries)	Flavour enhancer	☹	Asthma; hyperactivity; mood changes; itchy skin rashes up to 30 hrs after consuming; aspirin sensitive people may wish to avoid; not permitted in foods for babies; NRC; gout; kidney problems	Flavoured crisps, instant noodles, party pies	

Number	Names	Functions	Code	Potential Effects	Possible Food Use	Other Uses
636	**MALTOL** (synthetic; obtained by hydrogenation from maltose)	Flavour enhancer	😐?	Can cause a drop in the level of haemoglobin & an increase in haemosiderin; those with thalassaemia should avoid	Wine, tabletop sweeteners	Cigarettes
637	**ETHYL MALTOL** (made from maltol)	Flavour enhancer	😐?	*See Maltol (636)*	Some wines, tabletop sweeteners	Cigarettes
640	**GLYCINE** (nonessential amino acid; may be synthetic; may be of **ANIMAL** origin)	Flavour enhancer	😐?	May have beneficial health effects; in 2003 the FDA said it no longer regards it as safe in human foods?	Tabletop sweeteners, to mask aftertaste of saccharin	Animal feeds, supplements, cosmetics
641	**L-LEUCINE** (essential amino acid; may be of **ANIMAL** origin)	Flavour enhancer Antistatic	☺	Has beneficial effects in the body; excess may interfere with other substances in the body	Tabletop sweeteners	Permanent waves, hair conditioners
900a	**POLYDIMETHYLSILOXANE; DIMETHYLPOLYSILOXANE** (silicone; synthetic)	Anticaking agent Emulsifier	😐?	Acute or delayed hypersensitivity reactions; nausea; diarrhoea	Frying oils	Ointment base, topical drugs, barrier cream
901	**BEESWAX, WHITE AND YELLOW** (obtained from bees; or may be synthetic)	Glazing agent Emulsifier Emollient	☺	Regarded as safe in food use; can cause mild allergic reactions and contact dermatitis	Confectionery, chewing gum, surface treating fruits & vegetables	Mascara, eye shadow, baby creams, lipstick, cosmetics

Number	Names	Functions	Code	Potential Effects	Possible Food Use	Other Uses
903	**CARNAUBA WAX** (from a Brazilian wax palm tree)	Glazing agent	☺	Rarely causes allergic reactions; contact dermatitis; gastric irritation	Surface treatment of fruits and vegetables	Cosmetics, lipsticks, mascara, varnishes
904	**SHELLAC** (resin made by the Lac insect; of **ANIMAL** origin)	Glazing agent Binder	☺	Regarded as safe in foods; allergic contact dermatitis; skin irritation	Surface treatment of fruits and vegetables	Cosmetics, hair lacquer, tablets, mascara
905b	**PETROLATUM OR PETROLEUM JELLY** (petroleum derivative)	Glazing agent Lubricant	☹	Allergic skin reactions; may interfere with digestion and absorption of essential nutrients; it may cause discolouration of the skin when used topically	Processed foods	Lipsticks, baby cream & lotion, eye shadow, moisturiser, wax depilatories
914	**OXIDISED POLYETHYLENE** (synthetic; from petroleum)	Humectant Sealant	😐?	Carcinogenic?; kidney and liver damage?	Surface treatment of citrus fruits	
920	**L-CYSTEINE MONOHYDROCHLORIDE** (cysteine is derived from animal hair & chicken feathers; of **ANIMAL** origin)	Raising agent	☺	L-cysteine has health benefits; may provoke symptoms in those who react to MSG; has anti-insulin effects so caution advised in people with diabetes mellitus		L-cysteine is used in creams, shampoos, hair products; supplemental cysteine

Number	Names	Functions	Code	Potential Effects	Possible Food Use	Other Uses
941	**NITROGEN** (prepared from liquid air or from ammonia)	Propellant	☺☺	Regarded as safe in food use	Beer and related products	Preservative in cosmetics
942	**NITROUS OXIDE** (laughing gas)	Propellant	☺☺	Regarded as safe in food use	Flour (bleach), food aerosols	Whipped cosmetic creams
943a	**BUTANE** (petroleum derivative; greenhouse gas)	Propellant	😐?	Animal carcinogen; CNS depression; on NIH hazards list; neurotoxicity	Pressurised food containers	Aerosol cosmetics
943b	**ISOBUTANE** (petroleum derivative)	Propellant	😐?	*See Butane*	Pressurised food containers	Cosmetic sprays
944	**PROPANE** (petroleum derivative)	Propellant	😐?	May be narcotic in high concentrations; neurotoxicity	Pressurised food containers	Cosmetics in aerosols
946	**OCTAFLUOROCYCLOBUTANE** (used alone or with CO_2 or nitrous oxide)	Propellant	☺	Nontoxic when used alone	Pressurised food containers	
950	**ACESULPHAME POTASSIUM**	Sweetener	☹	Caused lung tumours, breast tumours, leukaemia, respiratory disease and cancer in animals	Flavoured milk, ice cream, edible ices, confectionery, jams, bakery products	Oral care products

Number	Names	Functions	Code	Potential Effects	Possible Food Use	Other Uses
951	**ASPARTAME** (prepared from phenylalanine and aspartic acid; breaks down to methanol then formaldehyde in the body; may be GM)	Sweetener Flavour enhancer	☹☹	Headache; depression; anxiety; asthma; fatigue; hyperactivity; MS like symptoms; blindness; aggression; migraine; insomnia; dizziness; irritability; epilepsy; memory loss; seizures; NRC and women during pregnancy; teratogenic	Processed foods, brewed soft drinks, confectionery, low joule foods; may be in anything labelled 'sugar free' or 'without added sugar'	Medications, including those for children
952	**CYCLAMATE OR CALCIUM CYCLAMATE OR SODIUM CYCLAMATE** (banned in some countries)	Sweetener	☹	Migraines; various skin conditions; urticaria; pruritis; may affect kidneys, heart, circulation, blood, reproduction, liver, thyroid; carcinogen	Sauces, toppings, jams, spreads, chutney, low joule chewing gum, jelly, brewed soft drink, sauces, toppings	
953	**ISOMALT** (produced from sugar)	Humectant Sweetener	☺	Regarded as safe in food use; may cause gastric irritation	Ice cream, jams, baked goods	Cosmetics
954	**SACCHARIN** (prepared from toluene; banned or restricted in many countries)	Sweetener	☹☹	Urticaria; pruritis; NRC; eczema; nausea; diarrhoea; diuresis; headache; mutagenic; carcinogenic; teratogenic	Jelly, brewed soft drinks, tabletop sweeteners, soup bases, sauces, toppings	Chewable aspirin, pharmaceutical preparations

Number	Names	Functions	Code	Potential Effects	Possible Food Use	Other Uses
955	**SUCRALOSE** (synthetically prepared from sugar and chlorine)	Sweetener	😐 ?	Thymus shrinkage; kidney and liver enlargement in animal studies	Confectionery, brewed soft drink	
956	**ALITAME** (synthetic; related to aspartame)	Sweetener	😐 ?	Reduced body weight gain and increased liver weight in animals	Custard mix, jelly, custard powder, ice cream, jams	
957	**THAUMATIN** (from the fruit of a West African plant; may be used with MSG)	Flavour enhancer Sweetener	☺ ☺	Regarded as safe in food use	Brewed soft drink, processed foods	
961	**NEOTAME** (synthetic; 7,000 - 13,000 times sweeter than sugar)	Sweetener	☹	Similar to Aspartame (951)	Confectionery, processed foods	
962	**ASPARTAME-ACESULPHAME SALT** (synthetic)	Sweetener	☹	*See Aspartame (951) and Acesulfame Potassium (950)*	Flavoured milk, ice cream, edible ices, jams, chutney	
965	**MALTITOL & MALTITOL SYRUP OR HYDROGENATED GLUCOSE SYRUP** (sugar alcohol made from malt sugar)	Sweetener Emulsifier Stabiliser Humectant	😐 ?	Increased incidence of tumours in rats; increase in breast cancer in female rats; raises blood sugar; may have a laxative effect	Low joule foods, dried fruit, confectionery	Cosmetics, brewing industry

Number	Names	Functions	Code	Potential Effects	Possible Food Use	Other Uses
966	**LACTITOL** (derived from milk sugar (lactose); **ANIMAL** origin)	Sweetener Humectant	☺☺	Regarded as safe in food use	Baked goods, chewing gum	
967	**XYLITOL** (formally from Birch wood, now made from waste products from the pulp industry)	Humectant Sweetener Stabiliser	☺	Regarded as safe in food use at low levels; reported to have beneficial effects on health; large doses may cause diarrhoea and flatulence	Ice cream, chocolate, jams, confectionery, chewing gum, toffee, mints	Toothpaste
968	**ERYTHRITOL** (produced by fermentation from glucose)	Sweetener Humectant	☺	Regarded as safe in foods; excess can have a laxative effect	Processed foods	Moisturising creams and lotions
1001	**CHOLINE SALTS** (choline is a water-soluble "B" group vitamin)	Emulsifier	☺	Regarded as safe in food use at low levels; choline has benefits on health; excess can lead to headaches, nausea, diarrhoea, arrhythmias, vertigo, muscle tension	Salt substitute	Supplements
1100	**ALPHA-AMYLASE** (digestive enzyme; may be of **ANIMAL** origin; may be **GM**)	Enzyme	☺☺	Regarded as safe in foods; has beneficial health effects	Flour for bread making	Cosmetics, supplements

Number	Names	Functions	Code	Potential Effects	Possible Food Use	Other Uses
1101	**PROTEASES** (ficin, bromelain, papain; may be **GM**)	Enzyme Stabiliser	😐 ?	Papain may cause allergic reactions; ficin may cause skin, eye & mucous membrane irritation; purging in large doses	Meat tenderiser, beer brewing, clotting milk	Antiinflammatory medication, supplements
1102	**GLUCOSE OXIDASE** (an enzyme; may be **GM**)	Antioxidant	😊 😊	No known adverse effects	Used in the making of sweeteners	Cosmetics
1104	**LIPASES** (digestive enzymes; of **ANIMAL** origin)	Enzyme	😊 😊	No known adverse effects	Cheese making	Supplements
1105	**LYSOZYME** (enzyme; may be from egg protein; of **ANIMAL** origin; may be **GM**)	Preservative Enzyme	😊	Has protective roles in thebody; may cause reactions in those allergic to egg protein	Processed foods, cheese preparation	Cosmeceuticals, skin conditioner, eye drops, lozenges
1200	**POLYDEXTROSE** (synthetic; includes citric acid, glucose & sorbitol; similar to cellulose)	Humectant Stabiliser Thickener	😊	Regarded as safe in food use at low levels; excess may have a laxative effect; NRC	Low joule foods, yoghurt, custard powder, ice cream, confectionery	Bulking ingredient in skin care products
1201	**POLYVINYLPYRROLIDONE** (plastic resin made using acetylene, hydrogen, formaldehyde, ammonia)	Stabiliser	☹ ☹	Lung & kidney damage; allergic contact dermatitis in sunscreen use; skin sensitisation	Tabletop sweeteners, beer, wine and vinegar manufacture	Hairsprays and lacquers, shampoos, sunscreens

Number	Names	Functions	Code	Potential Effects	Possible Food Use	Other Uses
1400	**DEXTRIN ROASTED STARCH** (synthetic; modified starch; *see Starch - Modified in section* 2)	Thickener Stabiliser	😐 ?	Uncertainties exist about the safety of modified starches, especially in infants	Confectionery, flour products other than bread	Cosmetics, matches, fireworks
1401	**ACID TREATED STARCH** (synthetic; modified starch; *see Starch - Modified in section* 2)	Thickener Stabiliser	😐 ?	May aggravate celiac disease; Uncertainties exist about the safety of modified starches, especially in infants	Processed foods	
1402	**ALKALINE TREATED STARCH** (synthetic; modified starch; *see Starch - Modified in section* 2)	Thickener Stabiliser	😐 ?	Uncertainties exist about the safety of modified starches, especially in infants	Processed foods	
1403	**BLEACHED STARCH** (synthetic; modified starch; *see Starch - Modified in section* 2)	Thickener Stabiliser	😐 ?	Uncertainties exist about the safety of modified starches, especially in infants	Processed foods	
1404	**OXIDISED STARCH** (synthetic; modified starch; *see Starch - Modified in section* 2)	Thickener Stabiliser	😐 ?	Uncertainties exist about the safety of modified starches, especially in infants	Casserole mix, batter mix, confectionery	

Number	Names	Functions	Code	Potential Effects	Possible Food Use	Other Uses
1405	**ENZYME TREATED STARCHES** (synthetic; may be **GM**; *see Starch - Modified in section 2*)	Thickener Stabiliser	😐?	Uncertainties exist about the safety of modified starches, especially in infants	Processed food	
1410	**MONOSTARCH PHOSPHATE** (modified starch; *see Starch - Modified in section 2*)	Thickener Stabiliser	😐?	Uncertainties exist about the safety of modified starches, especially in infants	Processed food	Antidandruff shampoo
1412	**DISTARCH PHOSPHATE** (modified starch; *see Starch - Modified in section 2*)	Thickener Stabiliser	😐?	Not to be used in infant formula; uncertainties exist about the safety of modified starches, especially in infants	Fruit pie fillings, instant puddings, instant desserts, chips, infant formula products	Cosmetics, water softener
1413	**PHOSPHATED DISTARCH PHOSPHATE** (synthetic; *see Starch - Modified in section 2*)	Thickener Stabiliser	😐?	Uncertainties exist about the safety of modified starches, especially in infants	Flavoured yoghurt, ice cream, infant formula products	
1414	**ACETYLATED DISTARCH PHOSPHATE** (synthetic; *see Starch - Modified in section 2*)	Thickener Stabiliser	😐?	Uncertainties exist about the safety of modified starches, especially in infants	Sauce, pickles, yoghurt, dry cake mix, infant formula products	

Number	Names	Functions	Code	Potential Effects	Possible Food Use	Other Uses
1420	**STARCH ACETATE** (modified starch; *see Starch - Modified in section 2*)	Thickener Stabiliser	😐 ?	Uncertainties exist about the safety of modified starches, especially in infants	Sauces, chutney, desserts, baked products, confectionery	Hair conditioner, skin conditioner
1422	**ACETYLATED DISTARCH ADIPATE** (modified starch; *see Starch - Modified in section 2*)	Thickener Stabiliser	😐 ?	Renal lesions and low growth rates in test rats; uncertainties exist about the safety of modified starches, especially in infants	Sauces, pickles, yoghurt, dry cake mix, canned fruits pie fillings, foods for infants, soups	
1440	**HYDROXYPROPYL STARCH** (may be **GM**; *see Starch - Modified in section 2*)	Thickener Stabiliser	😐 ?	Uncertainties exist about the safety of modified starches, especially in infants	Sauces, pickles, yoghurt, dry cake mix, infant formula products	
1442	**HYDROXYPROPYL DISTARCH PHOSPHATE** (may be **GM**; *see Starch - Modified in section 2*)	Thickener Stabiliser	😐 ?	Uncertainties exist about the safety of modified starches, especially in infants	Canned soups, frozen desserts, sauces, cake mix	
1450	**STARCH SODIUM OCTENYLSUCCINATE** (synthetic; *see Starch - Modified in section 2*)	Thickener Stabiliser	😐 ?	Uncertainties exist about the safety of modified starches, especially in infants	Essence, salad dressing, beverage whitener	

Number	Names	Functions	Code	Potential Effects	Possible Food Use	Other Uses
1505	**TRIETHYL CITRATE** (citric acid and ethyl alcohol)	Antifoaming agent	☺	Can provoke symptoms in those who react to MSG; citrates may interfere with the results of laboratory tests for blood, liver and pancreatic function	Eggs and egg products, food flavourings	Nail polish, perfume base, cigarettes
1518	**TRIACETIN** (obtained by adding acetate to glycerine; may be of **ANIMAL** origin)	Humectant	☺	Regarded as safe in food use; high dose injections proved fatal to rats	Coating for vegetables and fruits	Hair dyes, toothpaste, cigarette filters, perfumery
1520	**PROPYLENE GLYCOL** (made synthetically from propylene or glycerol or propylene oxide)	Humectant	☹	Contact dermatitis; lactic acidosis; dry skin; respiratory, immuno and neurotoxicity; CNS depression and kidney damage in animals	Surface treatment of citrus fruits	Suntan lotions, toothpaste, lipsticks, baby lotions, pesticides, antifreeze
1521	**POLYETHYLENE GLYCOL** 8000 (*see Polyethylene Glycol in section 2*)	Antifoaming agent	😐 ?	Has caused renal failure when used on burn victims; may be contaminated with 1,4-dioxane	Processing of certain foods	Antiperspirant, baby products, hair tonic, lipstick, protective cream, hair straightener

SECTION 2

COSMETIC INGREDIENTS

Names	Functions	Code	Potential Effects	Cosmetic Uses	Other Uses
ABIETIC ACID (abietol; from pine rosin)	Stabiliser Texturizer	😐?	Can cause allergic reactions; skin and mucous membrane irritation; harmful to marine life	Soapmanufacture, foaming face wash	Making vinyls, lacquers and plastics
ACETAL (derived from acetaldehyde)	Flavouring Solvent	☹	CNS depressant; respiratory depression; cardiovascular collapse; no known skin toxicity; possible high blood pressure; on NIH hazard list	Synthetic perfumes	Fruit flavouring in foods, hypnotic in medicine
ACETALDEHYDE (ethanal; may be of **ANIMAL** origin)	Solvent Intermediate	☹☹	Mucous membrane irritation; liver damage; kidney, respiratory and neurotoxicity; CNS depression; skin irritation; teratogenic; carcinogenic; harmful to aquatic organisms	Fragrance in cosmetics, perfume manufacture	Silvering of mirrors, synthetic rubber
ACETAMIDE MEA (n-acetyl ethanolamine)	Antistatic agent Humectant	😐?	Mild skin irritation; caused liver cancer in rats; may contain DEA; *see Diethanolamine*	Hair shampoos and conditioners, skin cream, hair tonic	
ACETAMINOPROPYL TRIMONIUM CHLORIDE	Antistatic agent	😐?	*See Quaternary Ammonium Compounds*	Shampoos, bath soaps, conditioners	Detergents
ACETARSOL (acetarsone)	Anti-microbial	😐?	Sensitisation; allergic reactions; lethal dose in mice is only 0.004g/kg of bw	Mouthwash, tooth-paste, feminine hygiene products	

Names	Functions	Code	Potential Effects	Cosmetic Uses	Other Uses
ACETIC ACID (occurs naturally in some fruits and plants)	Solvent Rubefacient	😐?	Skin irritation; hives; skin rash; caused cancer in rats & mice, orally and by injection; harmful to aquatic organisms	Hand lotions, hair dyes, freckle bleaching creams	
ACETONE (derived by oxidation or fermentation)	Solvent Denaturant	☹☹	Brittle nails; peeling & splitting nails; lung irritation; skin rashes; eye irritation; cardio-vascular, liver & neurotoxicity	Nail polish, nail polish remover	Solvent for air-plane glues, cellulose glues, paint thinners
ACETONITRILE (methylacyanide; precursor of cyanide; on Canadian Hotlist)	Solvent	☹☹	Nervous system poison; skin irritation; gastrointestinal and liver toxicity; teratogenic; fatal if swallowed	Artificial nails remover	Extraction processes
ACETYL TYROSINE (maybe of **ANIMAL** origin)	Biological Additive	☺☺	Nonessential amino acid; generally recognised as safe	Cosmetics, suntan creams and liquids	Dietary supplement
ACETYLATED LANOLIN (of **ANIMAL** origin; may be contaminated with pesticide residues)	Emulsifier Emollient	😐?	Undergoing review for safety; *see Lanolin*	Baby products, lip-sticks, cosmetic creams, eye make-up, hair conditioner	
ACETYLATED LANOLIN ALCOHOL (*see Acetylated Lanolin*)	Emulsifier Emollient	☺	Claimed to be hypo-allergenic; may be drying to the skin	Eye shadow, skin moisturisers, bath soaps, colognes	

Names	Functions	Code	Potential Effects	Cosmetic Uses	Other Uses
ACETYLMETHIONYL METHYL-SILANOL ELASTINATE (of **ANIMAL** origin)	Antistatic agent	☺☺	Considered safe in cosmetic use	Hair conditioners, skin conditioners	
ACID COLOURS EG ACID RED 14 (black, blue, brown, green, orange, red, violet , yellow; synthetic coal tar/azo dyes)	Hair dyes	☹	Many can cause skin, eye and mucous membrane irritation; *see Azo Dyes and Coal Tar*	Tints and dyes for hair colouring	
ACYLAMIDE COPOLYMER (acrylamide is derived from acrylonitrile & sulphuric acid)	Film former Thickener	☹	Acrylamide causes liver, reproductive and neurotoxicity; toxic by skin absorption; hazardous to the environment; especially harmful to fish	Nail enamels, cosmetics	
ACRYLATES COPOLOMER (synthetic, from petroleum)	Binder Film former	😐 ?	Acrylates are strong irritants	Nail polish, blusher, hairspray, mascara	
ALCOHOL (ethanol)	Solvent	😐 ?	Implicated in mouth, throat and tongue cancers; contact dermatitis; drying to the skin and hair if used in excess	Mouthwash, facial cleanser, perfumes, aftershave	Alcoholic beverages
ALKYL BENZENE SULFONATE	Detergent	😐 ?	Believed to be nontoxic orally; drying of the skin; may cause skin irritation	Shampoos, bubble baths	

Names	Functions	Code	Potential Effects	Cosmetic Uses	Other Uses
AHNFELTIA CONCINNA (derived from algae)	Botanical additive	☺☺	No known adverse effects	Skin conditioners, beauty aids	
ALLANTOIN (can be extracted from uric acid, found in comfrey root; may be of **ANIMAL** origin)	Anti-microbial Oral care agent	☺☺	May accelerate cell growth promoting healing of fractures, scars, wounds; may alleviate psoriasis	Cold creams, hand lotions, hair lotions, after-shave lotions, hair conditioners	
ALOE VERA, ALOE VERA GEL AND ALOE VERA EXTRACT	Botanical additive	☺☺	No known adverse effects; reputed to have beneficial and healing effects on the body	Skin creams, deodorants, soaps, shaving creams	
ALPHA HYDROXY ACIDS (AHA's; glycolic acid, lactic acid, tartaric acid, malic acid, citric acid, salicyclic acid, L-alpha hydroxy acid, mixed fruit acids and others; on Canadian Hotlist)	Exfoliant	☹	Long term skin damage; skin discolouration; swelling, especially around the eyes; skin blistering; itchiness; rashes; liver toxicity; photosensitivity; higher risk of skin cancer. Do not use on children or infants	Skin peels, skin toner, face and body creams, cuticle softeners, skin cleansers, skin improvers, shampoos	
ALUMINIUM ACETATE (mixture including acetic acid and boric acid)	Anti-microbial	☹	Skin rashes; severe sloughing of the skin; ingestion of large doses can cause diarrhoea, nausea, vomiting and bleeding; *see also Aluminium (173) in section 1*	Antiperspirants deodorants, barrier creams	Waterproofing, fabric finishes, dye for furs

Names	Functions	Code	Potential Effects	Cosmetic Uses	Other Uses
ALUMINIUM CHLORIDE (salt of aluminium)	Deodorant agent	☹	Skin irritation; allergic reactions; reproductive & neurotoxicity; teratogenic; harmful to aquatic organisms; *see also Aluminium (173) in section 1*	Lipsticks, antiperspirants	
ALUMINIUM CHLOROHYDRATE	Deodorant agent	☹	Contact allergic reactions; hair follicle infections; irritation of abraded skin; *see also Aluminium (173) in section 1*	Antiperspirants, deodorants	
ALUMINIUM ZIRCONIUM OCTACHLOROHYDRATE	Deodorant agent	☹	Harmful; contact allergic reactions; skin irritation; lung damage; granulomas; *see also Aluminium (173) in section 1*	Non-aerosol antiperspirants, deodorants	
AMBERGRIS (derived from sperm whales; of **ANIMAL** origin)	Fixative Flavouring	☺☺	Ambergris is 80% cholesterol; no known adverse effects in humans	Perfumery	Flavouring for foods & beverages, cigarettes
AMINOMETHYL PROPANOL (an alcohol made from nitrogen compounds)	Emulsifier	☺	Considered safe in cosmetic use up to 1% concentration; may cause skin irritation	Hairspray, shaving cream, cosmetic creams, deodorant	
2-**AMINO-4-NITROPHENOL** & 4-**AMINO-2-NITROPHENOL** (on Canadian Hotlist)	Hair colourant	☹	On a list of substances facing a ban by the EU; awaiting the submission of safety data; toxic to aquatic organisms	Orange-red and medium brown hair dyes	

Names	Functions	Code	Potential Effects	Cosmetic Uses	Other Uses
AMINOPHENOL (*m-,o-, p-*)	Colourant	☹	*See 2-Amino-4-nitrophenol*	Hair dyes	
AMMONIUM CARBONATE	Neutralizer Buffer	😐 ?	Skin rash on scalp, forehead and hands; contact dermatitis	Permanent wave solutions & creams	Fire extinguishers
AMMONIUM CHLORIDE	Acidifier Buffer	😐 ?	Possible skin and eye irritation in some people; toxic to aquatic organisms	Bubble baths, hair bleach, shampoos	Batteries, dyes, medicines
AMMONIUM COCOYL ISETHIONATE	Cleanser	☺	Considered safe in cosmetic use; may cause skin rashes	Soaps, shampoos	
AMMONIUM COCOYL SARCOSINATE (may be of **ANIMAL** origin)	Surfactant	😐 ?	May be contaminated with carcinogenic nitrosamines; *see Sarcosines*	Shampoos, dentifrices	
AMMONIUM HYDROXIDE (solution of ammonia and water)	Buffering agent Denaturant	😐 ?	Irritating to eyes and mucous membranes; may cause hair breakage; toxic by ingestion; harmful to the environment	Hair dyes, hair straightener, barrier cream, mascaras	Cigarettes, stain removers, detergents
AMMONIUM LAURETH SULPHATE	Surfactant	😐 ?	May be contaminated with carcinogenic nitrosamines	Shampoos, bubble baths, hand wash	Dishwashing liquid,detergent
AMMONIUM LAUROYL SARCOSINATE (may be of **ANIMAL** origin)	Surfactant	😐 ?	May be contaminated with carcinogenic nitrosamines; *see Sarcosines*	Shampoos, dentifrices	

Names	Functions	Code	Potential Effects	Cosmetic Uses	Other Uses
AMMONIUM LAURYL SULPHATE	Surfactant Foaming agent	😐 ?	Eye and skin irritation; repeated contact may dry the skin; may cause contamination with nitrosamines	Shampoos, bubble baths, liquid hand and body wash, toothpaste, bath gel	Dishwashing liquid, car wash detergent
AMMONIUM PERSULPHATE (ammonium salt)	Preservative Oxidiser	😐 ?	Asthma; mucous membrane and skin irritation; brittle hair	Cosmetics, dyes, skin lightener, soap	Detergents
AMMONIUM SULPHATE (ammonium salt)	Surfactant Cleanser	☹	Liver, neuro and respiratory toxicity; dry and denatured hair	Permanent wave lotions	Tanning, filler in vaccines
AMMONIUM THIOGLYCOLATE (ammonium salt of thioglycolic acid; on Canadian Hotlist)	Antioxidant	☹	Severe burns and blistering of the skin; hair breakage; cumulative irritant; severe allergic reactions; lethal to mice in large injected doses	Hair straighteners, depilatories, permanent wave solutions	
AMYL ACETATE (banana oil; obtained from amyl alcohol)	Solvent Flavouring	☹	Headache; fatigue; chest pain; CNS depression; neuro and respiratory toxicity; mucous membrane irritation	Perfumes, nail polish, nail polish remover	Banana flavouring in foods, perfuming shoe polish
AMYL DIMETHYL PABA (Padimate A)	UV absorber	☹	May cause sensitisation; increase breast cancer cell division; estrogenic; endocrine disruption; carcinogenic	Sunscreen preparations	

Names	Functions	Code	Potential Effects	Cosmetic Uses	Other Uses
ANETHOLE (from anise oil and others)	Flavouring Denaturant	😐 ?	Hives; skin blistering and scaling; gum and throat irritation	Perfume, toothpaste mouthwash	
AQUA (water)	Solvent	😊 😊	No adverse health effects, provided water is purified so it is not contaminated with chlorine, sodium fluoride etc	Many cosmetic and personal care products	Canned and bottled foods and beverages
ASCORBIC ACID (Vitamin C)	Antioxidant Preservative	😊 😊	Vitamin C plays many beneficial roles in the body	Cosmetic creams, antiwrinkle products	
ASCORBYL PALMITATE (derived form ascorbic acid)	Preservative Antioxidant	😊	Some palmitates may cause contact dermatitis	Cosmetic creams and lotions	
AZO DYES (extract from coal tar or crude oil; see coal tar)	Colourant	☹ ☹	Skin contact can cause hives, urticaria, asthma; hay fever; allergic reactions; bladder cancer; may be absorbed through the skin	Non-permanent hair rinses and tints	Foods and beverages
BALSAM PERU (extract from South American tree)	Antiseptic	😐 ?	Skin irritation, stuffy nose; contact dermatitis; common sensitiser; may cross-react with benzoic acid and others	Cream hair rinse, face masks, perfumes	Cigarettes
BARIUM SULPHATE	Depilatory agent	😐 ?	Often causes skin reactions, poisonous when ingested	Depilatories, cosmetics	

Names	Functions	Code	Potential Effects	Cosmetic Uses	Other Uses
Barium sulphide (on Canadian Hotlist)	Opacifier Depilating agent	☹	Skin rashes; chemical burns; never apply to inflamed skin; poisonous if ingested	Depilatories, hair relaxers, cosmetics	
Beeswax (from bees; of **animal** origin or may be synthetic)	Emulsifier Emollient	☺	Considered safe in cosmetic use; can cause mild allergic reactions & contact dermatitis	Lipsticks, mascara, baby creams, eye makeup, foundation	Confectionery, soft drinks, chewing gum
Behentrimonium chloride	Preservative	😐 ?	*See Quaternary Ammonium Compounds*	*See Quaternary Ammonium Compounds*	
Bentonite (white clay)	Thickener Emulsifier	😐 ?	Inert and generally nontoxic; may clog skin pores inhibiting proper skin function; venous injection causes blood clots and possibly tumours	Facial masks; makeup	Colourant in wine
Benzaldehyde (synthetic almond oil)	Solvent Flavouring	☹ ☹	Highly toxic; eye and skin irritation; allergic reactions; CNS effects; convulsions; kidney, liver, respiratory & neuro toxicity; on NIH hazards list; harmful to aquatic organisms	Cosmetic creams and lotions, soap, perfumes, dyes	Flavouring in sweets, cordials and ice cream, cigarettes
Benzalkonium chloride (BAK; on Canadian Hotlist)	Preservative Detergent	☹	TOXIC; eye and skin irriattion; contact dermatitis; conjunctivitis; can be fatal if ingested	Shampoos, hair conditioner, mouthwash, eye lotions	Antiseptic and detergent in medicinal use

Names	Functions	Code	Potential Effects	Cosmetic Uses	Other Uses
BENZENE (derived from toluene or gasoline; on Canadian Hotlist)	Solvent	☹☹	Highly toxic; liver, endocrine, immuno, respiratory & neuro-toxicity; skin rash & swelling; teratogen; carcinogenic; very toxic to aquatic organisms	Nail polish removers	Detergents, nylon, artificial leather, varnish, lacquer, oven cleaner, paint
BENZETHONIUM CHLORIDE	Preservative Antistatic agent	😐?	Endocrine toxicity; skin irritation; toxic to aquatic organisms; *see Quaternary Ammonium Compounds*	Cosmetics, feminine hygiene products	
BENZIN (from oil and coal)	Solvent Coating	☹	Chronic exposure can cause dizziness, headaches, loss of appetite		Protective coating on fruit and vegetables
BENZOPHENONES (1-12) (a dozen or more different ones exist)	Flavouring Fixative UV absorber	☹	Hives; photoallergic reactions; contact sensitivity; toxic when injected; on NIH hazards list; harmful to aquatic organisms	Hair sprays, soaps, sunscreen, perfume	Flavourings for various foods
BENZOYL PEROXIDE (from benzoic acid; on Canadian Hotlist)	Bleaching and drying agent	☹	Skin irritation; toxic if inhaled; allergic reactions; corrosive; AVOID SKIN CONTACT	Cosmetics, artificial nail kits	
BENZYL ACETATE (obtained from plants, especially jasmine)	Flavouring Solvent	☹	Vomiting; diarrhoea; eye and skin irritation; liver and neuro-toxicity; on NIH hazards list	Perfumes, soaps	Ice cream, baked goods, chewing gum

Names	Functions	Code	Potential Effects	Cosmetic Uses	Other Uses
BENZYL ALCOHOL (constituent of jasmine, hyacinth and other plants; synthetically derived from petroleum or coal tar)	Solvent Preservative Denaturant	☹	Headache; skin and mucous membrane irritation; neuro & liver toxicity; contact dermatitis; on NIH hazards list; toxic to aquatic organisms	Perfumes, hair dyes, shampoos, nail varnish remover	Fruit flavourings for foods, fabric softener, cigatettes
BENZYL CARBINOL (phenethyl alcohol)	Preservative	😐 ?	Eye irritation; toxic if ingested; sensitiser; birth defects in rats; CNS injury in mice	Cosmetics, most rose perfumes	Synthetic fruit flavouring in foods
BENZYL CINNAMATE (sweet Odour of Balsam)	UV absorber Additive	😐 ?	Cinnamates can cause a stinging sensation in some people; on NIH hazards list	Cosmetics, perfumes	Cigarettes, pesticides
BENZYLHEMIFORMAL	Preservative	😐 ?	Prolonged skin contact may be harmful	Cosmetics	
BENZYL SALICYLATE (synthetic)	UV absorber	😐 ?	Skin rash and swelling on exposure to sunlight	Sunscreens, perfumes	Cigarettes
BETAGLUCANS (found in oat fibre & barley)	Thickener	☺ ☺	No known adverse effects; may have beneficial effects	Facial powders, skin conditioners	
BETA-NAPHTHOL (from naphthalene from coal tar; on Canadian Hotlist)	Solvent	☹ ☹	Kidney damage, eye injury, convulsions, anaemia and death from ingestion; skin damage; contact dermatitis	Hair tonics, hair dyes, skin peels, perfumes	

Names	Functions	Code	Potential Effects	Cosmetic Uses	Other Uses
Beta hydroxy acids (**BHA**'s; **S**alicylic acid, beta hydroxy butanoic acid, tropic acid, trethocanic acid)	Exfoliant	😐 ?	Photosensitivity; skin reactions especially if skin is dry or sensitive; changes skin pH; do not use on children	Exfoliant creams, skin peels, skin masks, moisturisers	
BHA	Preservative	☹ ☹	*See Butylated Hydroxyanisole (320) in section 1*	Cosmetics	Foods
BHT	Preservative	☹ ☹	*See Butylated Hydroxytoluene (321) in section 1*	Cosmetics, lipstick, eyeliner, baby oil	Foods, packaging materials
Biotin (water soluble vitamin)	Texturiser Moisturiser	☺ ☺	No known adverse effects; beneficial effects on health	Cosmetic creams, hair conditioner	
Bismuth compounds (bismuth citrate, bismuth oxychloride etc)	Various	☹	Toxic effects include memory loss, convulsions, confusion, intellectual impairment; kidney and cardiovascular toxicity	Bleaching & freckle creams, nail polish, hair dyes	
Bisphenol A	Hardener	☹	Neurological diseases; learning difficulties; birth defects in mice; endocrine disruption; persists in the environment	Nail polish, cosmetics	Some plastic storage containers for foods and cosmetics
Borax (sodium tetraborate)	Emulsifier Texturiser	😐 ?	Chronic exposure can cause red peeling skin, seizures and kidney failure; harmful to aquatic organisms	Cold cream; shaving cream	Water softener, insecticide

Names	Functions	Code	Potential Effects	Cosmetic Uses	Other Uses
BORIC ACID (on Canadian Hotlist)	Anti-microbial	☹☹	Gastrointestinal, liver, kidney, reproductive, blood & neuro-toxicity; severe poisoning has occurred after ingestion and application to abraded skin	Baby powder, bath powder, eye cream, mouthwash, soap	Fungus control on citrus fruit
BROMATES (calcium, potassium, sodium bromate)	Maturing agent	☹	Respiratory depression; skin eruptions; kidney dysfunction and failure; effects on the CNS	Permanent wave neutraliser	Used in making bread
BROMOCHLOROPHENE (phenolic compound)	Preservative	☹	Acutely toxic when ingested; *see Hexachlorophene*	Cosmetics	
2-**BROMO**-2-**NITROPRO-PANE** 1,3-**DIOL** (Bronopol, BNPD)	Preservative Solvent	☹	Eye and skin irritation; liver toxicity; contact dermatitis; can produce carcinogenic nitrosamines & formaldehyde	Shampoo, mascara, eye makeup, liquid hand wash, nail polish, face creams	
5-**BROMO**-5-**NITRO**-1,3-**DIOXANE** (Bronidox L)	Preservative	☹	Skin and eye irritation; can release formaldehyde; can form nitrosamines	Shampoo, mascara, eye makeup, liquid hand wash	
BRONIDOX L	Preservative	☹	*See 5-Bromo-5-Nitro-1,3-Dioxane*	*See 5-Bromo-5-Nitro-1,3-Dioxane*	
BRONOPOL	Preservative Solvent	☹	*See 2-Bromo-2-Nitropropane-1, 3-Diol*	*See 5-Bromo-5-Nitro-1,3-Dioxane*	

Names	Functions	Code	Potential Effects	Cosmetic Uses	Other Uses
BUTANE (derived from petroleum)	Propellant	😐 ?	*See Butane (943a) section 1*	Aerosol cosmetics	Refrigerant
BUTYL ACETATE (synthetic; derived from butane)	Solvent Flavouring	☹	Toxic; can cause skin and eye irritation; conjunctivitis; irritation of respiratory tract	Perfumes, nail polish remover, eye shadow, soap	Synthetic flavouring in foods cigarettes
BUTYL ALCOHOL (synthetic; derived from butane)	Solvent Clarifier	☹	Contact dermatitis; dry skin; ingestion can cause mucous membrane irritation; drowsiness, headache, dizziness	Shampoos; nail products	Synthetic flavouring in foods, waxes, shellac, resin, cigarettes
BUTYLATED HYDROXYANISOLE	Preservative Antioxidant	☹☹	*See Butylated Hydroxyanisole (320) in section 1*	Cosmetics	Foods
BUTYLATED HYDROXYTOLUENE	Preservative Antioxidant	☹☹	*See Butylated Hydroxytoluene (321) in section 1*	Lipsticks, eyeliner, baby oils & lotions	Foods
BUTYLENE GLYCOL (synthetic)	Humectant Solvent	😐 ?	Not on the GRAS list of the FDA; ingestion may cause renal damage, vomiting, drowiness, depression, kidney damage, coma & death; may be harmful to the environment	Hairsprays, setting lotions	

Names	Functions	Code	Potential Effects	Cosmetic Uses	Other Uses
BUTYL MYRISTATE (from myristic acid and butyl alcohol)	Emollient	☺	May cause skin irritation; some myristates can promote acne	Lipstick, face cream, nail polish, nail polish remover	
BUTYLPARABEN (synthetic ester of p-hydroxybenzoic acid)	Preservative	☹	Allergic reactions; skin irritation; *see Parabens*	Cosmetics, shampoo	
BUTYROLACTONE	Solvent	☹	Toxic; possible human carcinogen; on NIH hazards list	Nail polish & polish remover, cosmetics	Making polyvinylpyrrolidone
C13-14 ISOPARAFFIN	Solvent	☺	Pure paraffin is thought to be harmless to the skin; impurities can cause eczema and irritation	Moisturiser, soaps, shaving products, sunscreen	
CAFFEINE (obtained as a byproduct of decaffeinated coffee)	Flavouring	☹	Liver, neuro, gastrointestinal, kidney and musculoskeletal toxicity; teratogenic; NRC; on NIH hazards list	Flavouring in lipsticks, helps other ingredients penetrate the skin	Liqueurs, cola soft drinks, chocolate, cigarettes
CALCIUM ACETATE (synthetic; salt of acetic acid)	Emulsifier	😐?	Allergic reactions; on NIH hazards list	Fragrances in cosmetics	Dyeing, tanning and curing skins
CALCIUM MYRISTATE (may be of **ANIMAL** origin)	Surfactant	☺	Considered safe in cosmetics; some myristates can promote acne	Cosmetics	

Names	Functions	Code	Potential Effects	Cosmetic Uses	Other Uses
CALCIUM SILICATE	Anticaking agent	😐 ?	Practically nontoxic orally; irritation of lungs & respiratory tract; allergic skin reactions	Face powders	Baking powder, limeglass
CALCIUM STEARATE (prepared from limewater)	Opacifier Colourant	☺	Considered safe in cosmetic use; being reviewed for safety	Shampoos, hair conditioners	Paints, printing ink, pesticides
CALCIUM SULFIDE (formed by heating gypsum with charcoal)	Depilating agent	☹	Toxic; skin and eye irritation; can cause allergic reactions; corrosive	Depilatories	Luminous paints
CALCIUM THIOGLYCOLATE	Depilating agent	☹	Harmful; skin problems on hands or scalp; hemorrhaging under skin; severe allergic reactions; thyroid problems in experimental animals	Permanent wave lotions, cream depilatories	Tanning leather
CALOMEL (mercurous chloride; banned from cosmetics in the EU and USA)	Bleaching agent	☹ ☹	Teratogenic; mercury poisoning; persists in the environment; very toxic to aquatic organisms; *see Mercury Compounds*	Skin bleaches, freckle cream; 'beauty creams'	
CAMPHOR OIL (banned in the USA for use as a liniment)	Preservative	☹	Spasms; convulsions; dizziness; liver and neurotoxicity; contact dermatitis; respiratory problems; foetal death	Hair tonic, after-shave and pre-shave lotions	Spice flavour in foods, embalming fluid, moth-balls

Names	Functions	Code	Potential Effects	Cosmetic Uses	Other Uses
CANTHAXANTHIN (may be of **ANIMAL** origin)	Colourant (pink)	😐 ?	Aplastic anaemia; oral intake can cause loss of night vision	Artificial tanning aids	Chicken feed to colour egg yoke
CAPRYLIC/CAPRIC/LAURIC TRIGLYCERIDE (may be of **ANIMAL** origin)	Emollient Solvent	☺	Low toxicity, mild eye and skin irritation	Lipsticks, bath oils, perfumes, soaps, hair sprays	
CAPTAN (derived from phenol)	Preservative	☹	Immuno and neurotoxicity; reproductive disorders; teratogenic; may be hazardous to aquatic and soil organisms	Soap, shampoo, cosmetics	Agricultural fungicide
CARBITOL	Humectant Solvent	☹	Hazardous at concentrations over 5%; more toxic than poylethylene glycol *(see)*	Sunscreen, nail enamel and lacquer	
CARBOMER 934, 940, 941	Thickener Emulsifier	😐 ?	Allergic reactions; eye irritation; safety under review	Cosmetics, toothpaste	Industrial uses
CARBOXYMETHYL CELLULOSE (made from cotton byproducts; may be **GM**)	Stabiliser Emulsifier	😐 ?	Toxicity when used in cosmetics is unknown; caused cancer and tumours in some animals studies	Shampoos, hand creams, shaving creams, hair grooming aids	Ice cream, beverages, laxatives
CASTOR OIL (from the seeds of the castor oil plant)	Plasticiser	😐 ?	Allergic reactions; ingestion can cause pelvic congestion and induce abortion	Lipsticks, bath oils, shaving cream, nail polish, face masks	Embalming fluid, laxatives, lamp oil

Names	Functions	Code	Potential Effects	Cosmetic Uses	Other Uses
CATECHOL (phenol alcohol in catechu black from acacia catechu)	Modifier	☹	Liver, cardiovascular, neuro and immunotoxicity; contact dermatitis; teratogenic; carcinogenic; toxic to aquatic organisms	Hair colouring, skin care preparations	
CERESIN WAX (brittle wax derived from the mineral ozokerite)	Thickener Antistatic agent	☺	Considered safe in cosmetic use; may cause sensitisation in some people	Barrier creams, hair conditioner, cream rouge, lipstick	Waxed paper and cloth, dentistry
CETALKONIUM CHLORIDE (derived from ammonia)	Preservative Antibacterial	😐 ?	Contact allergies; dry, brittle hair; ingestion can be fatal; *see Quaternary Ammonium Compounds*	Hair conditioners, deodorant cosmetics, antiperspirants	
CETEARETHS-3,-6,-12,-20, -25,-30,-33 (of **ANIMAL** origin)	Emulsifier Emollient	😐 ?	Skin dryness; allergic reactions; may be contaminated with the carcinogens 1,4-dioxane and ethylene oxide	Cosmetics, suntan products, shampoo, moisturisers, hair conditioners	
CETEARYL ALCOHOL (may be natural or synthetic; may be of **ANIMAL** origin)	Emulsifier Emollient	☺	May cause contact dermatitis and contact sensitisation in some people	Hair tints, lipsticks, shampoos, suntan preparations	
CETEARYL GLUCOSIDE (synthetic oleochemical from coconut & corn; may be **GM**)	Emulsifier	☺	*See Cetearyl Alcohol*	Hand and body preparations	

Names	Functions	Code	Potential Effects	Cosmetic Uses	Other Uses
CETEARYL PALMITATE (may be of **ANIMAL** origin)	Emollient	☺	Some palmitates may cause contact dermatitis	Hand lotion	
CETETH-1,-2,-4,-6,-10,-20, -30	Emulsifier Surfactant	😐 ?	May be contaminated with the carcinogens 1,4 dioxane and ethylene oxide *(see both)*	Hair products, skin care preparations, moisturisers	Detergents
CETRIMONIUM BROMIDE (synthetic)	Preservative	☹	Ingestion can be fatal; can cause skin and eye irritation; reproductive effects; teratogenic; toxic to mice embryos	Shampoo, deodorant, skin cleaning products	
CETRIMONIUM CHLORIDE (synthetic)	Preservative	😐 ?	*See Quaternary Ammonium Compounds*	Shampoo, hair conditioner	
CETYL ALCOHOL (synthetic oleochemical; may be of plant, **ANIMAL**, or petrochemical origin)	Emollient Emulsifier Opacifier	☺	Considered to have a low toxicity orally and on the skin; may cause hives and contact dermatitis; skin disorders	Baby lotions, mascaras, foundations, deodorant, antiperspirants, shampoos	Laxatives
CETYL LACTATE (may be synthetic; may be of **ANIMAL** origin)	Emollient	☺☺	No known toxicity or adverse reactions	Cosmetics	Pharmaceutical preparations
CETYL MYRISTATE (may be synthetic; may be of **ANIMAL** origin)	Emollient	☺	No known toxicity; may promote acne in some people	Cosmetics	

Names	Functions	Code	Potential Effects	Cosmetic Uses	Other Uses
CETYL OCTANOATE (may be of **ANIMAL** origin)	Emollient	☺	*See Cetyl Alcohol*	Cosmetic creams, lipsticks	Pesticides
CETYL PALMITATE (may be synthetic; may be of **ANIMAL** origin)	Emollient	☺	Considered safe in cosmetic use; some palmitates can cause contact dermatitis	Eye shadow, skin-care preparations	Manufacture of lubricants
CETYL RICINOLEATE (may be of **ANIMAL** origin)	Emollient Solvent	☺	Considered safe in cosmetic use; may cause eye irritation	Tanning preparations	
CETYL STEARATE (may be synthetic; may be of **ANIMAL** origin)	Emollient	☺☺	No known toxicity or adverse reactions	Skin conditioner in cosmetic products	
CHLORACETAMIDE (synthetic)	Preservative	😐?	*See Acetamide and Quaternary Ammonium Compounds*	Cold cream, mud packs, shampoo, cleansing lotions	
CHLORAMINE-T (synthetic)	Preservative Antiseptic	😐?	Skin irritation; allergic reactions	Mouthwashes, nail bleaches	
CHLORHEXIDINE (synthetic; on Canadian Hotlist)	Preservative Topical antiseptic	☹	Contact dermatitis; respiratory and immunotoxicity; has caused anaphylactic shock	Liquid cosmetics, feminine hygiene sprays, deodorant	

Names	Functions	Code	Potential Effects	Cosmetic Uses	Other Uses
CHLOROACETAMIDE (on Canadian Hotlist)	Preservative	☹	Allergic reactions; contact dermatitis; immunotoxicity	Cosmetics	
CHLOROBUTANOL (chlorbutanol; acetone chloroform)	Preservative Antioxidant	☹	Acute oral toxicity; CNS depression; allergic reactions; harmful if inhaled; can be absorbed into the skin	Eye lotions, baby oil	Treating mastitis in cows
p-**CHLORO**-*m*-**CRESOL**	Preservative	☹	Caused kidney damage and adrenal tumours in male rats; unsafe in cosmetic products	Skin care and suntan cosmetic products	
2-**CHLORO**-*p*-**PHENYLENE-DIAMINE**	Intermediate	☹ ☹	*See Phenylenediamine*	Hair dyes	
CHLOROTHYMOL (thymol derivative; phenolic compound)	Oral care agent Deodorant	😐 ?	Combined with chlorine can cause mucous membrane irritation and skin rashes; may be absorbed via the skin	Mouthwash, hair tonic, baby oils	Topical anti-bacterial medication
CHLOROXYLENOL (PCMX; synthetic)	Preservative Antibacterial	☹	Toxic by ingestion; liver and immunotoxicity; skin irritation; may be absorbed via the skin	Brushless shaving creams, shampoos, deodorants	Germicides, antifungal preparations
CHOLETH -10-24 (polyethylene glycol ether of cholesterol)	Emulsifier	☺	No known adverse reactions; safety is under review	Hand creams	

Names	Functions	Code	Potential Effects	Cosmetic Uses	Other Uses
CHROMIUM COMPOUNDS	Colourant	☹	Dust inhalation can cause irritation and ulceration; lung cancer years after exposure; allergic reactions	Green eye shadow, greenish mascara	
CI (NUMBER) EG **CI** 12085 (colour index; inorganic colour listing in the EU; mostly synthetic coal tar/azo dyes)	Colourant	😐 ?	Many can be harmful and cause skin, eye and mucous membrane irritation; *see Azo Dyes and Coal Tar*	Hair dyes	
CINNAMYL ALCOHOL (synthetic)	Flavouring Fragrance	☺	May cause allergic reactions	Synthetic perfumes, deodorants	Flavour in food, cigarettes
CINOXATE (cinnamic acid)	Flavouring UV absorber	😐 ?	Allergic skin rashes; photoallergic reactions	Sunscreens, perfumes	
CITRONELLA OIL (extract from fresh grass)	Flavouring Fragrance	😐 ?	Asthma; skin rash; hay fever; stuffy nose	Soaps, cosmetics, perfumes	Insect repellant, food flavouring
COAL TAR (contains creosol, quinoline, xylene, phenol, benzene, naphthalene and others)	Colourant	☹ ☹	Contact dermatitis; psoriasis; hives; phototoxicity; acne; skin rash; breast, bladder and liver cancers; harmful to the environment	Shampoo, hair dye, facial cosmetics, hand and body lotion, toothpastes	Adhesives, insecticides, creosotes, phenols
COCAMIDE DEA (semisynthetic)	Emulsifier Surfactant	☹	Allergic skin rash; can contain DEA *see Diethanolamine*	Shampoos, bubble bath, shaving gel	Pet shampoos

Names	Functions	Code	Potential Effects	Cosmetic Uses	Other Uses
COCAMIDE MEA (synthetic)	Surfactant Emulsifier	😐 ?	Mild skin reactions in some people; vapour is highly toxic; may contain nitrosamines; harmful to the environment	Shampoos, hair conditioners	
COCAMIDOPROPYL BETAINE (synthetic)	Surfactant	😐 ?	Contact dermatitis; allergic reactions; eyelid rash	Soap, eye makeup remover, shampoo	
COCAMIDOPROPYL DIMETHYLAMINE	Antistatic agent	😐 ?	Contact allergies; contact dermatitis in some people	Hair conditioners	
COCOAMIDOPROPYL HYDROXYSULTAINE	Surfactant Thickener	☺	May cause allergic skin rash; may contain nitrosamines	Shampoos, hair and skin creams	
COCOA BUTTER (theobroma oil; from roasted seeds of the cocoa plant)	Emollient Emulsifier	☺	Softens and lubricates the skin; may cause allergic skin reactions and cosmetic acne	Soaps, eyelash cream, rouge, nail whitener, lipsticks	Sweet sauces, confectionery, suppositories
COCO-BETAINE (synthetic; from coconut oil)	Surfactant	☺	May cause skin rash in sensitive people	Shampoos, face and hand gel	
COCO-POLYGLUCOSE (synthesised; may be GM)	Surfactant	☺	May cause skin irritation in sensitive people	Cosmetics	
COCONUT ACIDS, OIL AND ALCOHOLS (from coconut kernals)	Surfactant Emollient Solvent	☺	May alleviate dry skin; may cause allergic skin rashes; eye and skin irritation	Shampoos, baby soaps, massage creams	Margarine, chocolate, cigarettes

Names	Functions	Code	Potential Effects	Cosmetic Uses	Other Uses
COLLAGEN (of **ANIMAL** origin)	Biological additive	😐 ?	May form a film which can inhibit proper skin function; allergic reactions	Hand cream, moisturiser, cosmetics	
CORN FLOUR (may be **GM**)	Absorbant	☺	Used as a safer alternative to talc; when moist it can promote fungal & bacterial growth	Baby powder, face and bath powders	
CORN OIL (may be **GM**)	Emollient	☺	May cause allergic skin reactions in some people	Cosmetic creams, toothpaste	
CORN STARCH (may be **GM**)	Dusting powder	😐 ?	May cause allergic reactions; skin rashes; asthma; *see Corn Flour*	Dusting powders	Demulcent medication
COUMARINS (derived from tonka beans or made synthetically; banned in foods in the USA)	Fragrance Additive	☹	Allergic contact dermatitis; toxic by ingestion; photosensitivity; carcinogenic; teratogenic; on NIH hazards list	Acne preparations, soap, deodorant, hair dye, shampoo, sunscreen, perfume	Detergents
p-**CRESOL** (obtained from coal tar)	Preservative Flavouring	☹	Skin burns; dermatitis; respiratory failure; blood, endocrine, kidney, liver and neurotoxicity; less toxic than phenol; toxic to aquatic organisms	Mouthwash, cosmetics	Synthetic nut and vanilla flavour in foods

Names	Functions	Code	Potential Effects	Cosmetic Uses	Other Uses
CRYSTALLINE SILICA	Abrasive	☹	Eye, skin and lung irritation when used in its dry form; carcinogenic	Blusher, lip pencils, facial powder	'Kitty' litter, cleansers, paints
CRYSTALLINS (may be of **ANIMAL** origin)	Biological additive	☺☺	Currently no known adverse effects in cosmetic use	Hair and skin care products	
CYCLOHEXYLAMINE (synthetic)	Additive Buffer	☹	Cardiovascular, respiratory, reproductive, immuno and neurotoxicity; skin burns	Hairsprays	
CYCLOMETHICONE (silicone derived from silica)	Solvent Antistatic agent	😐?	No known toxicity, but it coats the skin which may inhibit proper functioning	Hair conditioner, lip-sticks, deodorants, skin fresheners	Waterproofing, lubricants
D & C COLOURS; **EG D & C RED NO.**6 (blue, brown, green, red, orange, violet and yellow)	Colourant	😐?	Most can cause health effects including skin rash, allergic reactions, asthma	Most cosmetics, including soaps, lip gloss, nail enamels	
DEA (diethanolamine)	Solvent Emulsifier	☹	*See Diethanolamine*	*See Diethanolamine*	
DEA CETYL PHOSPHATE (may be of **ANIMAL** origin)	Surfactant	☹	May contain DEA; *see Diethanolamine*	*See Diethanolamine*	
DEA COCAMIDE	Surfactant	☹	*See Cocamide DEA*	*See Cocamide DEA*	

Names	Functions	Code	Potential Effects	Cosmetic Uses	Other Uses
DEA LAURETH SULPHATE (synthetic or semi-synthetic)	Surfactant	☹	Harmful to aquatic organisms; *see Diethanolamine and Quaternary Ammonium Compounds*	Cosmetics, liquid soaps, shampoos, hair conditioners	
DEA LAURYL SULPHATE (synthetic or semisynthetic)	Surfactant	☹	Harmful to aquatic organisms; *see Diethanolamine and Quaternary Ammonium Compounds*	Cosmetics, liquid soaps, shampoos, hair conditioners	
DECYL ALCOHOL (derived from liquid paraffin)	Antifoamer Fixative	☺	Low toxicity on the skin in animal testing	Cosmetics, perfumes	Fruit flavouring in foods
DECYL MYRISTATE (may be of **ANIMAL** origin)	Emollient	☺	Myristates can promote acne in some people	Skin conditioner in cosmetics	
DECYL OLEATE (may be of **ANIMAL** origin)	Emollient Emulsifier	☺	May promote acne in some people; safety under review	Hand creams, sun-tan products	
DECYL POLYGLUCOSE (decyl alcohol and glucose)	Surfactant	☺	May cause skin irritation in sensitive people	Cosmetics	
DEXPANTHENOL (may be of **ANIMAL** origin)	Anti-inflammatory	☺☺	*See Panthenol*	*See Panthenol*	

Names	Functions	Code	Potential Effects	Cosmetic Uses	Other Uses
2,4-**DIAMINOANISOLE** (synthetic)	Hair dye	☹	Allergic contact dermatitis; mutagenic; carcinogenic	Hair dyes	
2,4-**DIAMINOPHENOL** (synthetic)	Hair dye	☹	*See Phenylenediamine*	Hair dyes	
DIAZOLIDINYL UREA (Germall II; of **ANIMAL** origin)	Preservative	☹	Sensitiser; contact dermatitis; eye and skin irritation; may release formaldehyde; not readily biodegradable	Shampoos, hair conditioners, shaving gel, moisturiser	Pesticides, textile industry
DIBEHENYLDIMONIUM CHLORIDE (synthetic)		😐?	*See Quaternary Ammonium Compounds*	*See Quaternary Ammonium Compounds*	
DIBENZOTHIOPHENE (from thioxanthrone; banned in cosmetics in Italy)	Additive	☹	CNS disorders; blood pressure problems; blood disorders	Antidandruff shampoos, acne products	Psychopharmaceutical products
DIBENZOYLMETHANES	UV absorber	😐?	Photoallergy; contact allergy	Sunscreens	
DIBROMOFLUORESCEIN (made by heating resorcinol with a naphthalene derivitive)	Colourant	☹	Sensitivity to light; skin rash; skin and eye inflammation; respiratory and gastro-intestinal symptoms	Indelible lipsticks	

Names	Functions	Code	Potential Effects	Cosmetic Uses	Other Uses
DIBROMOSALAN (banned in cosmetics in the USA)	Antiseptic Fungicide	☹	Light sensitivity resulting in skin rash and swelling	Toilet soaps, creams, lotions, powders	Detergents
DIBUCAINE	Local anesthetic	😐 ?	Highly toxic to rats when injected into the abdomen	Wax depilatories	
DIBUTYL OXALATE (synthetic)	Chelating agent	😐 ?	Oxalates are toxic	Products restricted to professional use	
DIBUTYL PHTHALATE (from phthalic acid isolated from a fungus; banned in nail polish in the EU)	Film former Solvent	☹ ☹	Liver, kidney, reproductive and neurotoxicity; abdominal pain; nausea; vertigo; contact allergic reactions; teratogen; carcinogenic; xenoestrogen; toxic to aquatic organisms	Perfume, nail polish, deodorant, antiperspirant	Insect repellant
DICETYLDIMONIUM CHLORIDE	Surfactant	😐 ?	*See Quaternary Ammonium Compounds*	Hair conditioner	
DICHLOROMETHANE (methylene chloride)	Solvent	☹ ☹	*See Methylene Chloride*	*See Methylene Chloride*	
DICHLOROPHENE (crystals from toluene)	Anti-microbial	☹	Harmful; developmental and neurotoxicity; skin rashes; allergic reactions	Shampoo, antiperspirant, deodorant	

Names	Functions	Code	Potential Effects	Cosmetic Uses	Other Uses
DICOCODIMONIUM CHLORIDE	Surfactant	😐 ?	*See Quaternary Ammonium Compounds*	*See Quaternary Ammonium Compounds*	
DICYCLOHEXYL SODIUM SULFOSUCCINATE	Surfactant	😐 ?	*See Quaternary Ammonium Compounds*	*See Quaternary Ammonium Compounds*	
DIDECYLDIMONIUM CHLORIDE	Surfactant	😐 ?	*See Quaternary Ammonium Compounds*	*See Quaternary Ammonium Compounds*	
DIETHANOLAMIDOOLEAMIDE DEA	Surfactant	☹	*See Quaternary Ammonium Compounds and DEA*	*See Quaternary Ammonium Compounds*	
DIETHANOLAMINE (DEA; *see Nitrosamines*)	Solvent Buffer	☹	Skin and mucous membrane irritation; cardiovascular, kidney, gastrointestinal, liver and neurotoxicity; can combine with nitrosating agents to form the carcinogenic nitrosamine NDELA; hormone disruption; on NIH hazards list; harmful to aquatic organisms	Cosmetics, soap, shampoo, hair conditioner, bubble bath, moisturising cream, liquid soap	Detergents

Names	Functions	Code	Potential Effects	Cosmetic Uses	Other Uses
DIETHYLENE GLYCOL (made by heating ethylene oxide with glycol)	Humectant Solvent	☹ ☹	Eye and skin irritation; ingestion can be fatal; blood, liver, kidney and neurotoxicity; teratogen; on NIH hazards list	Cosmetic creams, hair sprays	Paracetamol elixirs
DIETHYL PHTHALATE (made from ethanol and benzene derivatives)	Solvent Fixative Denaturant	☹ ☹	CNS depression; mucous membrane irritation; skin, liver, endocrine, respiratory and neurotoxicity; teratogen; may be hazardous to the environment, especially fish	Perfumes, nail polish	Insect repellant
DIHEXYL ADIPATE (from adipic acid)	Emollient Solvent	☺	Adipic acid has no known human toxicity but large oral doses are lethal to rats	Moisturisers, skin care products, makeup	
DIHYDROXYACETONE	Colouring Humectant	😐 ?	Allergic contact dermatitis; lethal in rats when injected	Artificial tanning preparations	
DIISOPROPANOLAMINE	Acid-alkali adjuster	😐 ?	On NIH hazards list; can combine with nitrosating agents to form nitrosamines	Hair dyes, permanent waves, tonics, hair grooming aids	Corrosion inhibitor
DIMETHICONE (created from silica using the petrochemical methanol)	Antifoaming agent Emollient	😐 ?	Low toxicity; skin irritation; allergic reactions; caused tumours and mutations in laboratory animals	Cosmetics, skin conditioners	Household detergents, topical drugs

Names	Functions	Code	Potential Effects	Cosmetic Uses	Other Uses
DIMETHYL PHTHALATE (phthalates are benzene derivatives)	Film former Solvent	☹	Phthalates linked with testicular cancer and cell mutations; neurotoxicity; can be absorbed through skin; teratogenic	Musk, calamine lotion, insect repellant	Pesticides
DIOCTYL PHTHALATE (phthalates are benzene derivatives)	Film former Solvent	☹	Phthalates linked with testicular cancer and cell mutations; CNS depression; teratogenic; bioaccumulation may occur in seafood	Perfumes, nail enamels	Pesticides
DIOCTYL SODIUM SULFOSUCCINATE	Surfactant	☺	Considered to be safe as presently used in cosmetics	Hair styling products	
1,4-**DIOXANE** (created during the manufacturing process; can be removed from products by vacuum stripping; on Canadian Hotlist)	Contaminant	☹☹	Hormone disruption; estrogen mimic; kidney, liver, neuro and cardiovascular toxicity; lowered sperm counts; can penetrate human skin; stress related illnesses; teratogenic; carcinogenic	May be in products with ingredients having polyethylene glycol, eth, polyoxyethylene, oxynol, polyethylene or PEG in their names	Pesticides
DIOXIN (TCDD; highly toxic and carcinogenic contaminant)	Contaminant	☹☹	Cardiovascular, liver, neuro, gastrointestinal, respiratory, immuno, endocrine and kidney toxicity; mutagen; teratogenic; carcinogenic	May be present in processed foods, chlorine bleached paper, plastic lined cartons and cans	Released when plastic is burnt, newsprint, pesticides

Names	Functions	Code	Potential Effects	Cosmetic Uses	Other Uses
DIPHENYL METHANE (from methylene chloride and benzene)	Fragrance	😐 ?	Local skin irritation; skin reaction to sunlight (prickling, swelling, pigmentation)	Perfumed soaps	
DIPHENYL OXIDE (synthetic; from benzene)	Chelating agent	😐 ?	Vapour toxic if inhaled	Perfumery, perfumed soaps	
DISODIUM LAURYL SULFOSUCCINATE	Surfactant	😐 ?	May cause contamination with carcinogenic nitrosamines	Shampoos, body wash, bubble bath	Household detergent
DISODIUM OLEAMIDE SULFOSUCCINATE (may be of ANIMAL origin)	Surfactant	😐 ?	May cause contamination with carcinogenic nitrosamines	Shampoos, body wash, bubble bath	Household detergent
DISTEARYLDIMONIUM CHLORIDE	Antistatic agent	😐 ?	*See Quaternary Ammonium Compounds*	*See Quaternary Ammonium Compounds*	
DMAE (in anchovies and sardines; may be of **ANIMAL** origin)	Emollient Firming agent	🙂 🙂	Supplemental DMAE is considered to have beneficial effects on health	Skin toners, face and eye creams, 'anti-aging' creams	Oral supplements
DMDM HYDANTOIN (derived from methanol)	Preservative	☹	Skin and eye irritation; allergic reactions; dermatitis; may release formaldehyde	Cosmetics, shampoos, mascara, cream conditioners	

Names	Functions	Code	Potential Effects	Cosmetic Uses	Other Uses
DODECYLBENZENE SULPHONIC ACID	Surfactant	😐?	Skin irritation and sensitisation; vomiting if ingested; toxic to aquatic organisms	Shampoos	Detergents
DODECYLBENZENYLTRIMONIUM CHLORIDE	Surfactant	😐?	*See Quaternary Ammonium Compounds*	*See Quaternary Ammonium Compounds*	
DODECYLHEXADECYLTRIMONIUM CHLORIDE	Antistatic agent	😐?	*See Quaternary Ammonium Compounds*	Hair conditioners	
DODECYLXYLDITRIMONIUM CHLORIDE	Antistatic agent	😐?	*See Quaternary Ammonium Compounds*	*See Quaternary Ammonium Compounds*	
DRIED EGG YOKE (of **ANIMAL** origin)	Colouring Protein	😐?	Allergic reactions including hives, eczema, anaphylaxis	Cosmetics	Root beer, soups, coffee
DROMETRIZOLE (derived from benzene)	Solvent UV absorber	☹	Determined not to be safe in cosmetic use by CIR Expert Panel; see *Benzene*	Nail polish, cosmetics	
EDTA	Sequestrant Preservative	😐?	*See Ethylene Diamine Tetraacetic Acid*	*See Ethylene Diamine Tetraacetic Acid*	
EGG POWDER (of **ANIMAL** origin)	Protein	☺	Harmless unless one is allergic to egg products	Shampoos, face masks, creams	

Names	Functions	Code	Potential Effects	Cosmetic Uses	Other Uses
ELASTIN (may be of **ANIMAL** origin)	Biological additive	☺	Considered safe in cosmetic use; may coat the skin inhibiting proper function	Shampoos, hair conditioner, skin creams & lotions	
EMU OIL (of **ANIMAL** origin)	Biological additive	☺☺	Reported to have beneficial effects on health	Hand cream, cosmetics	
EPO (Evening primrose oil)	Tonic	☺☺	*See Evening Primrose Oil*	*See Evening Primrose Oil*	
ETHANOL (ethyl alcohol; from the fermentation of carbohydrates)	Solvent Antibacterial	☹	Endocrine, cardiovascular, liver & neurotoxicity; dry skin; contact dermatitis; irritation	Toothpaste, mouthwash, nail enamel, hair spray, perfume	Laundry detergent, cigarettes
ETHANOLAMINES (mono, di and tri-forms)	Preservative Emulsifier	☹	Irritating to lungs, skin and eyes; hair loss; sensitisation; may be contaminated with carcinogenic nitrosamines	Hair dye, cold permanent-wave lotions, soap	
ETHOXYETHANOL (on Canadian Hotlist)	Solvent	☹	CNS depression; kidney damage; developmental, reproductive & neurotoxicity; can penetrate the skin	Cosmetics, nail enamel, shampoos	
ETHOXYETHANOL ACETATE (2-ethoxyethyl acetate)	Solvent	☹	Toxic, but less than ethoxyethanol; harmful to aquatic organisms; see *Ethoxyethanol*	Nail polish	

Names	Functions	Code	Potential Effects	Cosmetic uses	Other Uses
2-ETHOXYETHYL-P-CINNAMATE	UV absorber	😐 ?	*See Cinoxate*	*See Cinoxate*	
4-ETHOXY-M-PHENYLENE-DIAMINE SULPHATE	Hair dye	☹ ☹	*See Phenylenediamine*	*See Phenylenediamine*	
ETHYL ACETATE	Solvent Flavouring	☹	Skin irritation; prolonged inhalation can cause kidney & liver damage; neurotoxicity, drying & cracking of the skin	Perfumes, nail polish, nail polish remover	Synthetic flavour in foods, cigarettes, pesticides
ETHYL ALCOHOL	Solvent	☹	*See Ethanol*	*See Ethanol*	*See Ethanol*
ETHYLENEDIAMINE (synthetic; on Canadian Hotlist)	Solvent pH control	☹	Toxic if inhaled or absorbed by the skin; severe skin and eye irritation; asthma; contact dermatitis; sensitisation; harmful to aquatic organisms	Thigh creams, cosmetics	Metal polish, pesticides
ETHYLENEDIAMINE TETRAACETIC ACID (EDTA)	Sequestrant Preservative Chelating agent	😐 ?	Reported to have health benefits when used in chelation therapy; adverse effects can include asthma; skin and mucous membrane irritation; kidney damage; teratogen; on NIH hazards list; harmful to aquatic organisms	Hair dyes, shower gel, shampoos, bar soaps, face and hand gels	Oral supplements, carbonated beverages, dishwashing liquid, pesticides

Names	Functions	Code	Potential Effects	Cosmetic Uses	Other Uses
ETHYLENE GLYCOL	Solvent	☹	CNS depression; immuno, liver, neuro, respiratory, gastrointestinal and kidney toxicity; contact dermatitis	Perfume, liquid soap,cosmetics	Insect repellant, antifreeze, car wax, shoe products
ETHYLENE OXIDE (on Canadian Hotlist)	Humectant	☹☹	Liver, gastrointestinal, neuro, respiratory & kidney toxicity; headache; vomiting; spontaneous abortion; teratogen; mutagenic; carcinogenic; harmful to aquatic organisms	Cosmetics, shampoos	Fumigant used on ground spices & other processed natural seasonings
ETHYL ESTER OF PVM/PA COPOLYMER	Film former	☺☺	Considered safe as presently used in cosmetics	Hair setting preparations	
ETHYL METHACRYLATE (ester of ethyl alcohol and methacrylic acid; on Canadian Hotlist)	Thickening agents	☹	Skin irritation; allergic reactions; neurotoxicity; allergic contact dermatitis; teratogen; AVOID SKIN CONTACT	Nail polish, artificial nails	
ETHYL MYRISTATE (ethyl alcohol & myristic acid; may be of **ANIMAL** origin)	Emollient Flavouring	☺	Considered safe in cosmetic use; some myristates can promote acne	Cosmetics	Flavouring in foods, cigarettes
ETHYL PALMITATE (may be of **ANIMAL** origin)	Emollient Flavouring	☺	Considered safe in cosmetic use; some palmitates can cause contact dermatitis	Cosmetics	Flavouring in foods, cigarettes

Names	Functions	Code	Potential Effects	Cosmetic Uses	Other Uses
ETHYLPARABEN (ethyl p-hydroxybenzoate; synthetic)	Preservative	☹	Allergic reactions; skin irritation; contact dermatitis; moderate potential for bio-accumulation; *see Parabens*	Cosmetics, makeup, shampoo, deodorant	
ETHYL SALICYLATE	Flavouring	😐?	Allergic reactions, especially in people allergic to other salicylates	Perfumes	Flavouring in foods, cigarettes
ETHYL THIOGLYCOLATE (synthetic)	Depilatory agent	☹	Thioglycolates can cause skin irritations, hair breakage, severe allergic reactions	Depilatories	
EUCALYPTUS OIL (from the fresh leaves of the eucalyptus tree)	Local antiseptic	😐?	Can cause allergic reactions and skin irritation; large oral doses (1 tsp) can be fatal	Skin fresheners	Flavourings in foods, local antiseptic
EUGENOL (obtained from clove oil)	Additive Fixative	😐?	Allergic reactions; vomiting and gastric irritation if ingest-ed; liver and neurotoxicity	Perfumes, dentrifices	Flavourings in foods
EUXYL K 400	Preservative	😐?	There have been reports of allergic reactions; allergic contact dermatitis?	Cosmetics, toiletries	
EVENING PRIMROSE OIL	Tonic	☺☺	Believed to have beneficial health effects	Cosmetics	

Names	Functions	Code	Potential Effects	Cosmetic Uses	Other Uses
FARNESOL (found in star anise, cassia, citronella, rose, balsam and others)	Additive Flavouring	😐 ?	Considered safe in current use; mildly toxic by ingestion; caused mutations in laboratory animals	Perfumery	Flavouring in foods, cigarettes
FERROUS SULPHATE	Antiseptic Flavouring	☹	Gastrointestinal, liver, kidney, cardiovascular & neurotoxicity; teratogenic; carcinogenic?	Hair dye, cosmetics	Flavouring in foods, treatment of anaemia
FICIN (an enzyme from in the latex of tropical trees; may be GM)	Meat tenderiser	😐 ?	Skin, eye and mucous membrane irritation	Used in cosmetics as a protein digestant	Cheese, to clot milk
FLUORESCEIN	Colouring	☹	Lip inflammation; photosensitivity; respiratory and gastrointestinal symptoms	Indelible lipstick, nail polish	Dying wool, silk and paper
FLUORIDE (cumulative poison; classified as a contaminant by the USEPA; on Canadian Hotlist)	Oral care Preservative Insecticide	☹☹	Hypothyroidism; arthritis; osteoporosis; carpal tunnel syndrome; impaired brain function; birth defects; hip fractures; stress fractures; liver, kidney, musculoskeletal and neurotoxicity; dental and skeletal fluorosis; teratogen; carcinogenic	Toothpaste, cosmetics, mouthwash, dentrifices	Many products containing water eg soft drink, cordial, fruit juice, canned & bottled foods, public water supplies, dental treatments

Names	Functions	Code	Potential Effects	Cosmetic Uses	Other Uses
FORMALDEHYDE (gas derived from the oxidation of methyl alcohol; banned in cosmetics in some countries; on Canadian Hotlist)	Preservative Anti-microbial	☹ ☹	Eye, nose and throat irritation; coughing; nose bleeds; liver, respiratory, immuno, skin, reproductive and neurotoxicity; nausea; contact dermatitis; rash; asthma; on NIH hazards list; teratogenic; carcinogenic	Mascara, nail hardener, nail polish, soap, hair restorer, shampoo, antiaging creams, bubble baths, deodorants	Furniture polish, car wax, filler in vaccines, defoaming agents, animal feeds
GERANIOL AND GERANYL COMPOUNDS	Additive Flavouring	😐 ?	Allergic reactions; contact dermatitis; toxic if ingested	Perfume, shampoo, cosmetics	Chewing gum, cigarettes
GERANIUM OIL (extract from plants)	Botanical additive	😐 ?	Contact dermatitis and skin irritation in some people; ingestion can be fatal	Tooth powder, dusting powder, perfume	Ointments
GLUTARAL	Preservative Germicide	☹ ☹	*See Glutaraldehyde*	*See Glutaraldehyde*	*See Glutaraldehyde*
GLUTARALDEHYDE (glutaral; synthetic; amino acid occurring in green sugar beets)	Preservative Germicide	☹ ☹	Contact allergic reactions; contact dermatitis; immuno, developmental, reproductive, skin and respiratory toxicity; nausea; headache; aches and pains; palpitations; mood swings; asthma; teratogenic; very toxic to aquatic organisms	Antiperspirant, hair spray, deodorant, setting lotion, waterless hand soaps	Food flavouring; disinfectant used in hospitals and dentistry

Names	Functions	Code	Potential Effects	Cosmetic Uses	Other Uses
GLYCERIN, GLYCEROL (may be a byproduct of soap manufacture; may be from plants, or of **ANIMAL** origin)	Humectant	☺	Considered nontoxic and non-allergenic; may cause skin to dry out in low humidity; skin irritation in some people	Hand creams, face masks, barrier creams	Various food uses
GLYCERYL DISTEARATE (from glycerin & stearic acid may be of **ANIMAL** origin)	Emulsifier Emollient	😐?	May cause allergic reactions; contact dermatitis	Skin freshener, mascara, shampoo, cuticle softeners	
GLYCERYL MYRISTATE (may be of **ANIMAL** origin)	Emulsifier Stabiliser	😐?	May cause contact dermatitis; may promote acne	Baby cream, face masks, hand lotion	
GLYCERYL OLEATE (may be of **ANIMAL** origin)	Emulsifier Emollient	😐?	May cause contact dermatitis and skin allergies	Cosmetic creams and lotions	
GLYCERYL PABA (may be of **ANIMAL** origin)	UV absorber	😐?	May cause contact dermatitis and photosensitivity	Sunscreens	
GLYCERYL STEARATE (may be of **ANIMAL** origin)	Emulsifier Emollient	😐?	May cause skin allergies; contact dermatitis	Makeup, cuticle softeners	
GLYCERYL THIOGLYCOLATE	Depilatory agent Reducing agent	☹	Contact dermatitis; thioglycolates can cause hair breakage, skin irritations, severe allergic reactions	Permanent wave solutions, depilatories	

Names	Functions	Code	Potential Effects	Cosmetic Uses	Other Uses
Glycolic acid (made synthetically from chloroacetic acid)	Buffer Exfoliant	😐 ?	Mildly irritating to skin and mucous membranes; may cause sun sensitivity; exfoliative dermatitis; NRC	Skin peelers, exfoliants	Dying, brightening copper
Guar hydroxypropyl-trimonium chloride	Antistatic agent	😐 ?	*See Quaternary Ammonium Compounds*	*See Quaternary Ammonium Compounds*	
Hectorite (clay containing lithium and magnesium silicates; constituent of bentonite)	Absorbant Antistatic agent	☺	Considered safe in cosmetic use; dust can cause lung irritation	Hair bleaches, eye liners, foundations	Pesticides
Hedera helix (extract from English Ivy)	Botanical Toning agent	😐 ?	Can cause severe skin rashes; blistering; itching; contact dermatitis	Bath products, face and hand creams	
Heliotropin (piperonal; purple diazo dye)	Additive Flavouring	😐 ?	Allergic reactions; skin irritation; CNS depression on ingestion of large amounts	Perfumes, soaps	Cherry and vanilla food flavours
Hemp seed oil (from the hemp plant)	Emollient	☺☺	No known adverse effects in cosmetic use	Lip balms, skin moisturisers	
Henna (from the ground-up dried leaves and stems of a shrub)	Hair dye (red)	☺	One of the safest hair dyes; may cause allergic skin rash, avoid use near the eyes	Hair dye, conditioner and rinse	

Names	Functions	Code	Potential Effects	Cosmetic Uses	Other Uses
HEXACHLOROPHENE (prohibited in most cosmetic products in the EU and USA; on Canadian Hotlist)	Preservative	☹☹	Multiple sclerosis; contact dermatitis; gastointestinal, liver and neurotoxicity; birth defects; asthma; blindness; chloasma; allergic reactions; very toxic to aquatic organisms; bioacculates in the food chain eg milk; possible long term environmental effects	Antiperspirant, deodorants, baby oils, shampoos, toothpaste, cold cream, baby powders	Washing fruit, detergents, animal products
HEXYLENE GLYCOL (synthetic)	Solvent Viscosity controlling agent	☹	Contact dermatitis; eye, skin and mucous membrane irritation; gastrointestinal, liver, neuro and respiratory toxicity	Cosmetics	Pesticides
HEXYLRESORCINOL (derived from petroleum)	Antioxidant Antiseptic	☹	Severe gastrointestinal irritation; bowel, liver and heart damage; allergic reactions	Mouthwash, sunburn creams	Antiworming medicine, antiseptic
HOMOSALATE (homomethyl salicylate)	UV absorber	😐?	Endocrine disruption; reports of poisonings when absorbed through the skin	Sunscreens	
HYALURONIC ACID (natural protein found in the body; of **ANIMAL** origin)	Humectant Antistatic agent	☺☺	Considered to have beneficial health effects	Skin moisturisers, eye creams, hair conditioners	Oral supplements

Names	Functions	Code	Potential Effects	Cosmetic Uses	Other Uses
HYDRAZINE (from chloramine, ammonia and sodium hydroxide;on Canadian Hotlist)	Reducing agent	☹	Toxic if inhaled, ingested or absorbed through the skin; kidney, liver, cardiovascular, immuno and neurotoxicity; carcinogenic; teratogenic; very toxic to aquatic organisms	Cosmetics	
HYDROGEN PEROXIDE (made from barium peroxide and diluted phosphoric acid; on Canadian Hotlist)	Preservative Oxidising agent	😐?	Generally recognised as safe as a preservative in cosmetics; corrosive to skin, eyes & respiratory tract when undiluted; may cause allergic reactions, headache; nausea; toxic to aquatic orgamisms	Mouthwash, skin bleach, toothpaste, cold cream, hair bleach	Cheddar and Swiss cheese, medicinal antiseptic and germicide
HYDROLYSED PROTEIN (of **ANIMAL** origin; contains MSG)	Flavouring Flavour enhancer	😐?	Can cause contamination with carcinogenic nitrosamines; *see MSG (621) in section 1*	Cosmetics, shampoo and hair treatments	Animal feed
HYDROLYSED VEGETABLE PROTEIN (derived from whey, it contains 10-30% MSG; may be **GM**)	Flavour enhancer Antistatic agent	😐?	Concerns associated with HVP include decreased body weight, organ atrophy, behavioural overactivity and bladder & bowel incontinence	Hair care products	Canned tuna, soup, sauces, packet meals

Names	Functions	Code	Potential Effects	Cosmetic Uses	Other Uses
HYDROQUINONE (a phenol that occurs naturally, but is usually made synthetically from benzene; on Canadian Hotlist)	Antioxidant Bleaching agent	☹ ☹	Nausea, vomiting, delirium & collapse from ingestion; eye damage; contact allergy; contact dermatitis; sensitisation; liver toxicity; mutagen; very toxic to aquatic organisms	Freckle creams, suntan lotions, hair colouring	Pesticides
***p*-HYDROXYANISOLE** (derived from hardwood tar or made synthetically; on Canadian Hotlist)	Antioxidant	☹	Non-Hodgkin's lymphoma; skin depigmentation; ingestion can cause intestinal tract irritation and heart failure; eye and skin irritation	Permanent hair colour, lipsticks	Antiseptic
HYDROXYETHYLCELLULOSE (made from cellulose using petrochemicals; may be **GM**)	Binder Film former	☺	Considered safe in cosmetic use; adverse reactions rare	Shampoos, tanning, products, mascara, hand & body lotions	
HYDROXYMETHYL GLYCINATE	Preservative	😐 ?	May release formaldehyde; *see Formaldehyde*	Cosmetics	
HYDROXYMETHYL-CELLULOSE	Thickener Additive	☺	Considered safe in cosmetic use; adverse reactions rare	Cosmetics, hair care products	
HYDORXYPROPYL METHYLCELLULOSE (made from cellulose using petrochemicals)	Film former	☺	Considered safe in cosmetic use; mild eye and skin irritation; allergic reactions	Bubble bath, hair care products, tanning preparation	

Names	Functions	Code	Potential Effects	Cosmetic Uses	Other Uses
IMIDAZOLIDINYL UREA (of **ANIMAL** origin)	Preservative	☹	Contact dermatitis; may release formaldehyde; see *Formaldehyde*	Baby shampoo, eye shadow, bath oil, moisturiser, rouge	
ISOBUTANOL (isobutyl alcohol)	Solvent	☹	Toxic by inhalation; skin and mucous membrane irritation; dermatitis; neurotoxicity	Shampoos, fragrances	Synthetic fruit flavourings, cigarettes
ISOBUTYL ALCOHOL	Solvent	☹	*See Isobutanol*	*See Isobutanol*	*See Isobutanol*
ISOBUTYL MYRISTATE (may be of **ANIMAL** origin)	Emollient	☺	Myristates can promote acne in some people	Cosmetics	
ISOBUTYL PALMITATE (may be of **ANIMAL** origin)	Emollient	☺	Palmitates can cause contact dermatitis in some people	Cosmetics	
ISOPROPANOL (isopropyl alcohol; derived from petroleum)	Solvent Antifoaming agent	☹	Dry and denatured hair, skin irritation; liver, respiratory, gastrointestinal, kidney and neurotoxicity; teratogenic	Hair colour rinse, hand lotion, after-shave lotion, nail enamel	Antifreeze, room deodorisers, shellac, carpet cleaner, car wax
ISOPROPANOLAMINE (MIPA)	pH control Solvent	☹	Severe skin and eye irritation; contact allergy and dermatitis; may form nitrosamines	Cosmetic creams	Insecticides
ISOPROPYL ALCOHOL	Solvent	☹	*See Isopropanol*	*See Isopropanol*	*See Isopropanol*

Names	Functions	Code	Potential Effects	Cosmetic Uses	Other Uses
ISOPROPYL ISOSTEARATE (may be of **ANIMAL** origin)	Emollient	☺	Considered safe in cosmetic use; skin irritation when undiluted; may promote acne see *Stearic Acid*	Skin conditioners, skin cleansers	
ISOPROPYL LANOLATE (of **ANIMAL** origin)	Lubricant Emollient	😐?	May cause skin sensitisation; safety is under review	Cosmetics, skin cream, lipstick	
ISOPROPYL LINOLEATE (may be **GM**)	Emollient	☹	CIR Expert Panel concluded there is insufficient data to support safety in cosmetics	Skin conditioner in cosmetics	
ISOPROPYL MYRISTATE (may be of **ANIMAL** origin)	Emollient Solvent	☹	May significantly increase the absorption of the carcinogen NDELA; may promote acne; on NIH hazards list	Suntan lotions, bath oil, shampoo, hand lotions, deodorants	Pesticides
ISOPROPYL PALMITATE (may be of **ANIMAL** origin)	Emollient Preservative	😐?	Eye and skin irritation; allergic reactions; on NIH hazards list	Moisturiser, baby lotion, cologne, hair care products	Pesticides
ISOPROPYL STEARATE (may be of **ANIMAL** origin)	Emollient Binder	😐?	May cause skin irritation and allergic reactions	Skin conditioners	Pesticides
ISOSTEARYL NEOPENTANOATE (may be of **ANIMAL** origin)	Emollient	☺	Considered safe in cosmetic use; may promote acne	Eye makes, foundations	

Names	Functions	Code	Potential Effects	Cosmetic Uses	Other Uses
ISOSTEARYL PALMITATE (may be of **ANIMAL** origin)	Surfactant Emollient	☺	May be a sensitiser for people who suffer allergies; may cause contact dermatitis	Hand cream, shaving cream, soap, protective cream	
ISOTHIAZOLINONE	Preservative	😐 ?	May cause allergic reactions and contact dermatitis	Cosmetics	
KAOLIN (China clay)	Anticaking agent Absorbent	😐 ?	May inhibit proper skin function by clogging the pores; chronic inhalation can affect the lungs leading to fibrosis	Baby powder, bath powder face powder, makeup	Making pottery, porcelain, bricks
KATHON CG (methylisothiazolinone and methylchloroisothiazolinone)	Preservative	☹	Contact dermatitis; potent sensitiser; bacterial mutagen; skin cancer	Shampoo, cosmetics	Leather preservation
KERATIN (of **ANIMAL** origin; on Canadian Hotlist)	Film former Additive	☺	Considered safe for most people when used in cosmetics	Permanent wave, shampoo, hair rinse and conditioner	
LANOLIN; LANOLIN OIL; LANOLIN WAX (may be contaminated with pesticides; of **ANIMAL** origin)	Emulsifier Emollient	😐 ?	Thought to be safe if uncontaminated; may cause allergic skin reactions, acne and contact dermatitis	Lipstick, mascara, nail polish remover, eye shadow, hair conditioner	Pesticides
LARD OIL (of **ANIMAL** origin)	Emollient	☺☺	Considered safe in cosmetic use	Shaving cream, soaps	Chewing gum base

Names	Functions	Code	Potential Effects	Cosmetic Uses	Other Uses
LATEX (synthetic rubber)	Film former	😐 ?	Skin rash; allergic reactions; anaphylaxis; ingredients of latex compounds can be poisonous	Beauty masks	Chewing gum base, gloves, balloons, condoms
LAURALKONIUM CHLORIDE	Preservative	😐 ?	Can cause eye irritation; may form nitrosamines	Should not be in products containing nitrosating agents	
LAURAMIDE DEA (synthetic derivative of coconut oil)	Thickener Foam booster	☹	Itchy scalp; allergic skin reactions; dry hair; may contain DEA; *see Diethanolamine*	Shampoo, hair conditioner, bubble bath	Dishwashing detergent
LAURAMIDE MEA (synthetic derivative of coconut oil)	Antistatic agent	😐 ?	May cause mild skin irritation; may contain DEA; *see Diethanolamine*	Shampoo, hair conditioner	Dishwashing detergent
LAURAMIDOPROPYL BETAINE	Antistatic agent	😐 ?	*See Quaternary Ammonium Compounds*	*See Quaternary Ammonium Compounds*	
LAURAMINE OXIDE	Antistatic agent	😐 ?	Can form carcinogenic nitrosamines	Hair care products	
LAUROYL LYSINE (may be of **ANIMAL** origin)	Viscosity controlling agent	☺ ☺	Considered safe in cosmetic use	Facial powders	

Names	Functions	Code	Potential Effects	Cosmetic Uses	Other Uses
LAURYL ALCOHOL (derived from coconut oil)	Surfactant Emollient	😐 ?	Skin irritation; may promote acne	Perfume, shampoo	Detergents
LAURYL SULPHATE (derived from lauryl alcohol)	Foam booster	😐 ?	Skin sensitisation; moderate toxicity by ingestion; may contain formaldehyde	Shampoos	
LAVENDER OIL (from the fresh flowery tops of the lavender plant)	Fragrance	☺	Considered to have beneficial effects on health; may cause allergic contact dermatitis; photosensitivity?	Shampoos, skin fresheners, mouthwash, perfumes, dentrifices	Antiseptic oils, creams and lotions, cigarettes
LEAD ACETATE (made from lead monoxide and acetic acid)	Hair dye	☹ ☹	Lead poisoning; liver, kidney and neurotoxicity; effects brain development in infants and children; carcinogenic; toxic to aquatic organisms, bioaccumulates in plants & animals; persists in the environment	Hair dyes, hair colour restorer for men	Skin treatment in animals, printing colours
LINALOOL (extract from oils of lavender, bergamot and coriander)	Additive	😐 ?	May cause allergic reactions; facial psoriasis; mildly toxic by ingestion; skin and eye irritation; may effect the liver	Perfumes, cologne, perfumed soaps, after shave, hand lotion, hairspray	Flavouring in foods, cigarettes, fabric softener
LINOLEAMIDE DEA (diethanolamine and linoleic acid)	Emulsifier	☹	Can contain DEA; *see Diethanolamine*	Should not be in products containing nitrosating agents	

Names	Functions	Code	Potential Effects	Cosmetic Uses	Other Uses
LINOLEAMIDE MEA (mixture of ethanolamides of linoleic acid)	Antistatic agent	😐 ?	May be irritating to the skin and eyes; may contain DEA; *see Diethanolamine*	Hair care products	
LINOLEIC ACID (from edible fats and oils; may be of **ANIMAL** origin)	Emulsifier Antistatic agent	☺	No known adverse effects in cosmetics; nausea and vomiting if large amounts ingested	Cosmetics	Vitamins, digestive aids, cheese making
LINSEED OIL (from flaxseed)	Emollient	😐 ?	Cosmetic acne; allergic reactions	Shaving cream, medicinal soap	Paint, varnish, linoleum
MAGNESIUM LAURETH SULPHATE	Surfactant	😐 ?	May cause mild irritation to skin and eyes; may contain carcinogens 1,4 dioxane and ethylene oxide *(see both)*	Shampoos	
MAGNESIUM MYRISTATE (magnesium salt of myristic acid)	Opacifier	☺	Myristates may promote acne in some people	Cosmetics	
MAGNESIUM OLETH SULPHATE (of **ANIMAL** origin)	Surfactant	😐 ?	May contain carcinogens 1,4 dioxane and ethylene oxide *(see both)*	Cosmetics	Detergents
4-MBC (methyl-benzylidene camphor)	UV absorber	☹	Endocrine disruptor; estrogenic; increased uterine activity in pre-pubescent rats	Sunscreens	

Names	Functions	Code	Potential Effects	Cosmetic Uses	Other Uses
MENTHOL (may be natural or synthetic)	Flavouring	😐 ?	Allergic reactions; skin irritation; concentrate toxic if ingested; on NIH hazards list	Skin fresheners, perfumes, mouth wash	Chewing gum, cigarettes, pesticides
MERCAPTANS (compounds with reduced sulphur bound to carbon)	Fragrance	☹ ☹	Highly toxic; skin irritation; allergic reactions; infections of hair follicles	Depilatories	
MERCURY COMPOUNDS (prohibited in most cosmetic products in the USA; on Canadian Hotlist)	Preservative	☹ ☹	Extremely toxic; blood, liver, kidney, neuro, respiratory and reproductive toxicity; autism; epilepsy; teratogenic; can be absorbed through the skin; mercury is very toxic to aquatic organisms; bioaccumulates especially in fish	Medicated soap, cosmetics, freckle cream, face masks, hair tonic, eye preparations	Dyes, paint, fungicides, plastics
METHACRYLIC ACID (on Canadian Hotlist)	Primer	☹	Poisonous if ingested; skin & nail damage; inflammation; burns; infection; neurotoxicity	Artificial nail kits; nail products	
METHANOL	Solvent	☹	*See Methyl Alcohol*	*See Methyl Alcohol*	
METHENAMINE (made from formaldehyde and ammonia)	Preservative Antiseptic	☹	Can release formaldehyde; nitrosamine precursor; skin irritation; skin rash	Deodorant creams and powders, mouthwash	Medicines

Names	Functions	Code	Potential Effects	Cosmetic Uses	Other Uses
METHICONE (silicone)	Antistatic Emollient	😐 ?	*See Dimethicone*	Lipstick, blusher, mascara, after-shave	
METHOXYETHANOL (ethylene glycol ether; on Canadian Hotlist)	Solvent Fragrance	☹	Developmental and reproductive toxicity; birth defects, on NIH hazards list		
4-METHOXY-M-PHENYLENE-DIAMINE (4-MMPD; on Canadian Hotlist)	Hair dye	☹ ☹	CIR Expert Panel concluded that it is unsafe as a cosmetic ingredient; *see Phenylenediamine*	*See Phenylenediamine*	
4-METHOXY-M-PHENYLENE-DIAMINE SULPHATE (4-MMPD sulphate; on Canadian Hotlist)	Hair dye	☹ ☹	CIR Expert Panel concluded that it is unsafe as a cosmetic ingredient; *see Phenylenediamine*	*See Phenylenediamine*	
5-METHOXYPSORALEN (5-MOP; banned from cosmetics in the EU)	UV absorber	☹	Increased risk of skin cancer; contact allergy; photoallergy; neurotoxicity; carcinogenic	Suntan accelerator, sunscreens	
8-METHOXYPSORALEN (8-MOP; banned from cosmetics in the EU)	UV absorber	☹	Contact allergy; photoallergy; liver and neurotoxicity; carcinogenic	Suntan accelerator, sunscreens	

Names	Functions	Code	Potential Effects	Cosmetic Uses	Other Uses
METHOXYSALEN (8-methoxypsoralen)	UV absorber	☹	*See 8-Methoxypsoralen*	Suntan accelerator, sunscreen	
4-METHOXYTOLUENE -2, 5-DIAMINE HCL	Fragrance Flavouring	☹	*See Toluene*	Perfumes	Flavouring in foods
METHYL ACETATE (occurs naturally in coffee)	Solvent	😐?	Neurotoxicity; skin dryness, chafing and cracking	Perfumes, toilet waters	
METHYL ALCOHOL (methanol; on Canadian Hotlist)	Solvent Denaturant	☹	Eczema; dermatitis; cardio-vascular, liver, respiratory, endocrine and neurotoxicity; teratogen	Shampoos	Antifreeze, ink, paint, varnish, shellac, paint stripper
METHYL ANTHRANILATE (synthetic, from coal tar)	Fragrance Flavouring	😐?	Skin irritation; on NIH hazards list; *see Coal Tar*	Perfumes, suntan lotions	Food flavour, cigarettes
METHYLCHLOROISOTHIAZO-LINONE (on Canadian Hotlist)	Preservative	😐?	May cause allergic reactions; contact dermatitis; mutagen? see *Kathon CG*	Shampoo, liquid hand and body wash, after-shave	Dishwashing liquid
METHYLDIBROMO GLUTARONITRILE	Preservative	☹	Considered unsafe for use in cosmetic products; allergic reactions; contact dermatitis; skin sensitisation	Hair conditioner, bubble bath, indoor tanning preparation	Dishwashing liquid

Names	Functions	Code	Potential Effects	Cosmetic Uses	Other Uses
Methylene chloride (dichloromethane; on Canadian Hotlist)	Fragrance	☹☹	Nausea; dizziness; eye and skin irritation; dermatitis; neuro, liver, cardiovascular, kidney, endocrine & respiratory toxicity; carcinogenic; teratogenic; environmental hazard; possible ground water contamination	Nail enamel, hair conditioner, shampoos, hairspray, cleansing creams	Tablet coatings, anaesthetic in medicine, decaffeination of some coffees
Methyl ethyl ketone (MEK; synthetic; usually from butyl alcohol)	Solvent Fragrance	☹	Irritating to eyes, skin and mucous membranes; CNS depression; headache; liver and neurotoxicity; dermatitis	Shampoo, hair conditioner, nail polish, perfume	Paint thinners, adhesives
Methyl isobutyl ketone (MIBK)	Flavouring Fragrance	☹☹	Hazardous by ingestion or inhalation; kidney, gastrointestinal, respiratory, liver and neurotoxicity; dermatitis; birth defects; carcinogenic	Perfumes	Synthetic fruit flavouring in foods, solvent for cellulose and lacquer
Methylisothiazolinone (on Canadian Hotlist)	Preservative	😐?	*See Isothiazolinone and Methychloroisothiazolinone*	Baby products, hand wash, shampoos	Dishwashing liquid
Methyl methacrylate (banned in the EU; on Canadian Hotlist)	Film former	☹☹	Severe skin irritation; allergic reactions; contact dermatitis; liver, blood, respiratory, kidney, reproductive, neuro and immunotoxicity; teratogenic; harmful to aquatic organisms	Nail polish, artificial nails	Medical and dental orthopaedic cement, adhesives

Names	Functions	Code	Potential Effects	Cosmetic Uses	Other Uses
METHYL METHACRYLATE CROSSPOLYMER	Film former	☹	*See Methacrylic Acid*	Nail products	
METHYLPARABEN (methyl p-hydroxybenzoate)	Preservative	☹	May cause allergic reactions; contact dermatitis; *see Parabens*	Many cosmetic and personal care products	
METHYL SALICYLATE (Oil of Wintergreen; may be synthetic)	Flavouring Disinfectant	☹	Strong irritant to the skin and mucous membranes; blood, liver, neuro, reproductive and respiratory toxicity; teratogen; harmful to aquatic organisms	Toothpaste, mouthwash, sunburn lotion	Flavour in foods, detergents, cigarettes
MEXENONE (2-Hydroxy-4-methoxy-4'-methyl-benzophenone)	UV absorber	😐?	Photoallergy; hives; contact allergy; chronic actinic dermatitis; can mimic or exacerbate an illness; *see Benzophenones*	Sunscreens	
MICA (pulverised silicate minerals)	Opacifier Colouring	😐?	May cause irritation and lung damage if powder inhaled; gastrointestinal & liver toxicity	Face powder, eye cosmetics, lipstick, shampoo, mascara	
MILK (may be contaminated with traces of pesticides, GMO's, antibiotics and hormones; of **ANIMAL** origin)	Emollient	😐?	May cause allergic reactions from mild to severe; in cosmetic use it can cause pimples and acne if not rinsed thoroughly from the skin	Bath preparations, face masks, face wash	Hidden? (cream of rice, filled candy bars, macaroni, items with casein)

Names	Functions	Code	Potential Effects	Cosmetic Uses	Other Uses
MINERAL OIL (white oil; petroleum derivative)	Emollient	☹	Can inhibit proper functioning of the skin; dry skin; teratogenic; kidney and neurotoxicity when untreated or mildly treated; may be phototoxic	Baby creams and lotions, lipsticks, cold creams, eye creams	Used as a food additive in some countries
MIXED FRUIT ACIDS	Exfoliating agent	☹	*See Alpha Hydroxy Acids*	*See Alpha Hydroxy Acids*	*See Alpha Hydroxy Acids*
MONOETHANOLAMINE (MEA; ingredients ending in MEA)	Humectant Emulsifier	😐?	Can cause skin and eye irritation; may cause carcinogenic nitrosamine formation	Soaps, cosmetics	Detergents, paint stripper
MONTAN WAX (derived from lignite)	Emulsifier	☺	Considered nontoxic in cosmetic uses	Lipsticks, foundations	
MORPHOLINE (prepared from diethanolamine; on Canadian Hotlist)	Emulsifier Surfactant	☹	Skin, eye and mucous membrane irritation; kidney, liver, respiratory and neurotoxicity; *see Diethanolamine*	Various cosmetics	Coating on fresh fruit and vegetables
MOSKENE	Fragrance	☹	*See Musk Moskene*	*See Musk Moskene*	
MUSK (dried secretion from a deer; of **ANIMAL** origin)	Fragrance	☺	Generally safe and nontoxic; can cause allergic reactions in some people	Perfumes	Flavouring in foods

Names	Functions	Code	Potential Effects	Cosmetic Uses	Other Uses
MUSK AMBRETTE (of **ANIMAL** origin; banned from cosmetics in the EU)	Fixative Flavouring	☹	Neurotoxic; photosensitivity; contact dermatitis; serious brain damage in animals	Cosmetic creams, aftershave lotions, soaps, dentrifices	Food flavouring, detergents
MUSK MOSKENE (of **ANIMAL** origin; banned from cosmetics in the EU)	Fragrance	☹	Can cause non-permanent hyperpigmentation; pigment-ed contact dermatitis	Perfumes, rouges	
MYRISTALKONIUM CHLORIDE (may be of **ANIMAL** origin)	Surfactant Preservative	😐?	*See Quaternary Ammonium Compounds*	*See Quaternary Ammonium Compounds*	
MYRISTAMIDE DEA (may be of **ANIMAL** origin)	Viscosity control	☹	*See Diethanolamine*	*See Diethanolamine*	
MYRISTIC ACID (may be of **ANIMAL** origin)	Emulsifier	😐?	Can cause skin irritation; mut-ations in laboratory animals	Shampoos, shaving creams and soaps	Food flavour, cigarettes
NANOPARTICLES (see also Glossary)	UV absorber	😐?	May cause DNA damage; bioaccumulate; cause brain damage in aquatic species	Cosmetics, barrier creams, sunscreen	
1-NAPHTHOL (coal tar derivative)	Hair dye	☹	Toxic by ingestion and skin absorption; very toxic to aq-uatic organisms; *see Coal Tar*	Hair dyes, perfumery	Treatments for skin diseases

Names	Functions	Code	Potential Effects	Cosmetic Uses	Other Uses
Neem seed oil (from a tree native to India)	Antibacterial Antiviral	☺	Improves dry skin, eczema, acne & dandruff; teratogen?	Skin cream, soap, lipstick, shampoo	Insect repellant
Neomycin (antibiotic; antibiotics are banned from cosmetics in the EU	Antibiotic	☹☹	Can cause allergic reactions, photoallergy, kidney toxicity, may promote staph infections	May be used in some underarm deodorants	
Neotame	Sweetener	☹	*See Neotame (961) section 1*		
Nerol	Fragrance	😐?	*See Geraniol*	Perfumes	Flavouring foods
Niacinamide (specific form of vitamin B3)	Additive	☺	Considered to have many beneficial effects on health	Hair conditioners, anti-aging products	Cereal flours
Nickel sulfate	Additive	☹	Skin rash; kidney, endocrine and immunotoxicity; vomiting if ingested; contact dermatitis	Hair dyes, eye pencils, cosmetics, astringents	Mineral supplement, nickel plating
Nitrates (sodium, potassium etc)	Preservative Colour fixative	☹☹	May combine with amines found in the stomach, saliva, foods and cosmetics to form carcinogenic nitrosamines		Cured meats, matches, tobacco
Nitrites (sodium, potassium etc)	Preservative Colour fixative	☹☹	May combine with amines found in the stomach, saliva, foods and cosmetics to form carcinogenic nitrosamines	Sodium nitrite is used as an anticorrosive in some cosmetics	Cured meats, matches, tobacco

Names	Functions	Code	Potential Effects	Cosmetic Uses	Other Uses
NITROBENZENE (essence of mirabane; nitric acid and benzene; on Canadian Hotlist)	Fragrance Solvent	☹☹	Cyanosis; drowsiness; headaches; nausea; reproductive, kidney, liver, respiratory and neurotoxicity; absorbed throught the skin; teratogenic	Cheap scented soaps	Making analine a base for dyes and drugs, shoe polish
2-NITRO-*p*-PHENYLENE DIAMINE (derived from coal tar)	Hair dye	☹☹	*See Phenylenediamine*	*See Phenylenediamine*	
NITROSAMINES (toxic group of compounds formed when nitrites and nitrates combine with amines; eg NDELA may be found in cosmetics and shampoos; on Canadian Hotlist)	Contaminant	☹☹	Can cause many forms of cancer including liver, lung, mouth, stomach and esophageal; liver damage; can pass through the skin; environmental effects not adeqately investigated	Cosmetic products and shampoos with DEA, MEA or TEA compounds unless removed by the manufacturer	Found in air, tobacco smoke, pesticides, water, cured meats
NYLON (synthetic)	Thickener Opacifier	☺	Generally regarded as safe in cosmetic use, may cause allergic reactions in some	Mascara, eye shadow, highlighter, eyelash lengtheners	
OCTYL DIMETHYL PABA (PadamateO)	UV absorber	😐?	May cause sensitisation; increase breast cancer cell division; estrogenic; endocrine disruption; carcinogenic	Sunscreens, makeup	

Names	Functions	Code	Potential Effects	Cosmetic Uses	Other Uses
OCTYL DODECANOL (may be of **ANIMAL** origin)	Solvent Surfactant	☺☺	Generally regarded as safe in cosmetic use	Hair conditioner, lipsticks	
OCTYL METHOXYCINNAMATE	UV absorber	😐?	Photoallergy and contact allergy; endocrine disruption	Sunscreen, lipstick, perfume, foundation	
OCTYL PALMITATE (may be of **ANIMAL** origin)	Emollient	☺	Generally regarded as safe; may cause cosmetic acne	Cold cream, shaving cream, lipstick	
OLEAMIDE DEA (may be of **ANIMAL** origin)	Viscosity control	😐?	Urticaria; can cause carcinogenic nitrosamine formation; *see Diethanolamine*	Shampoo, bubble bath, lipstick, soap	
OLEIC ACID (may be of **ANIMAL** origin)	Emollient Defoaming agent	☺	Low oral toxicity; may cause mild skin and eye irritation; may promote acne	Soft soap, lipstick, cosmetics	Cigarettes
OLEOYL SARCOSINE (may be of **ANIMAL** origin)	Antistatic agent Surfactant	😐?	Can cause mild skin irritation; sarcosines can enhance absorption of other ingredients through the skin & can cause nitrosamine contamination	Soaps, cosmetics, lubricants, hair conditioners	Polishing compounds
OLESTRA (Olean; synthetic fat substitute; may be of **ANIMAL** origin)	Artificial fat substitute	☹	Abdominal cramps; nausea; diarrhoea; flatulence; muscular degeneration; inhibits absorption of nutrients		Low fat spread, french fries, ready-to-eat savoury snacks

Names	Functions	Code	Potential Effects	Cosmetic Uses	Other Uses
OLETH 2 - OLETH 50 (of **ANIMAL** origin)	Emulsifier Surfactant	😐 ?	Some oleths cause allergic reactions; limited information	Range of cosmetics and personal care	
OLIVE OIL (obtained from ripe olives)	Emollient Emulsifier	☺	Generally safe; may cause allergic reactions and acne	Shampoo, lipstick, soap, hair oil	Massage oil
ORANGE OIL (from the fresh peel of the sweet orange)	Fragrance Flavouring	☺	Allergic reactions if hyper-sensitive; severe reactions to concentrated oil of orange	Perfumery, soaps, colognes	Cigarettes, pesticides
ORRIS ABSOLUTE (from stems of the iris plant)	Fragrance	☺	Generally safe; can cause allergic reactions	Perfumes	
ORTHOPHENYLPHENOL (O-phenylphenol)	Anti-microbial	☹	Very toxic; mutagenic; skin irritation; carcinogenic	Cosmetics	Disinfectant sprays
OXYBENZONE (derived from isopropanol)	UV absorber	😐 ?	Photosensitivity; chronic actinic dermatitis; contact allergy	Sunscreens	
OXYQUINOLINE SULFATE (made from phenols)	Preservative	☹	*See Phenol*	Cosmetics	
PABA (on Canadian Hotlist)	UV absorber	😐 ?	*See Para-aminobenzoic Acid*	*See Para-aminobenzoic Acid*	*See Para-aminobenzoic Acid*
PADIMATE A (amyl dimethyl PABA)	UV absorber	☹	*See Amyl Dimethyl PABA*	Sunscreens	

Names	Functions	Code	Potential Effects	Cosmetic Uses	Other Uses
PADIMATE O (octyl dimethyl PABA)	UV absorber	☹	*See Octyl Dimethyl PABA*	Makeup, sunscreens	
PANTHENOL (may be of **ANIMAL** origin)	Antistatic agent	☺☺	Considered to have beneficial health effects	Hair care products, cosmetics	Digestive aid
PAPAIN (from papaya; may be **GM**)	Additive	☺	Considered to have health benefits; skin irritation	Skin creams, skin scrubs, skin masks	Meat tenderiser
PARA-AMINOBENZOIC ACID (found in vitamin B complex; on Canadian Hotlist)	UV absorber	😐?	Helps prevent UV damage to skin and hair; photosensitivity; contact dermatitis; eczema; increase risk of skin cancer?	Sunscreen, sunburn lotion, shampoo, hair conditioner	Treatment for arthritis
PARABENS (butyl, ethyl, methyl, propyl etc; synthetic; esters of hydroxybenzoic acid)	Preservative	☹	May cause allergic reactions; endocrine disruption; contact dermatitis; possible increase in the risk of breast cancer; toxic in animals by ingestion	Many cosmetic and personal care products	Various processed foods
PARAFFIN (from petroleum, wood, coal or shale oil)	Emollient Viscosity control	😐?	Pure paraffin is nontoxic to the skin; impurities can cause skin irritation and eczema	Lipsticks, mascara, eyelash cream	Pesticides
PBSA (2-phenylbenzimidazole-sulphonic acid)	UV absorber	😐?	Skin damage; may increase the risk of skin cancer	Sunscreens	

Names	Functions	Code	Potential Effects	Cosmetic Uses	Other Uses
PECTIN (found in roots, stems and fruits of plants)	Thickener Binder	☺☺	Considered to have beneficial effects on health	Toothpastes, hair setting lotions, barrier creams	Foods, anti-diarrheal medicine
PEG COMPOUNDS EG PEG-20 MYRISTATE (polyethylene glycols or polymers of ethylene oxide)	Solvent Emulsifier	☹	Can be contaminated with 1,4-dioxane, ethylene oxide, lead and arsenic; *see Polyethylene Glycols*	Many cosmetic and personal care products	Manufacture of surfactants
PEPPERMINT OIL (from the plant mentha piperita)	Flavouring	😐?	Can cause allergic reactions; hay fever; skin rash; allergic contact dermatitis	Toothpaste, shaving lotion	Foods and beverages, cigarettes
PETROLATUM (WHITE) (petroleum jelly; from petroleum)	Emollient Antistatic agent	☹	Allergic skin reactions; skin discolouration; may contain the cancer causing contaminants poylcyclic aromatics	Wax depilatories, cold creams, eye shadow, lipsticks	Glazing agent on some foods, pharmaceuticals
PHENOL (carbolic acid; derived from coal tar)	Preservative Denaturant	☹☹	Respiratory, cardiovascular, kidney, liver and neurotoxicity; paralysis; rash; nervous disorders; carcinogenic; toxic to aquatic organisms	Mouthwash, hand lotion, sunburn lotion, soap, shaving cream	Disinfectants
PHENOXYETHANOL (derived from phenol and ethylene oxide)	Preservative	😐?	Mild allergic skin rashes in sensitive people; concentrated solutions can cause headache, nausea, renal failure	Shampoo, liquid soap, bubble bath, cosmetics, perfume	Insect repellant, antifreeze, filler in vaccines

Names	Functions	Code	Potential Effects	Cosmetic Uses	Other Uses
PHENYLALANINE (essential amino acid; found in eggs, legumes, dairy products etc)	Artificial sweetener Antistatic	😐 ?	Sufferers of phenylketonuria (PKU), melanoma or cirrhosis need to restrict intake; PKU, if not detected early can lead to mental deterioration in children	Hair conditioners	Some artificial sweeteners, cigarettes
PHENYLBENZIMIDAZOLE SULPHONIC ACID	UV absorber	☹	*See PBSA*	*See PBSA*	
PHENYLENEDIAMINE (*m*-,*o*-*p*-) (on Canadian Hotlist)	Hair dye	☹ ☹	Eczema; asthma; skin rash; gastritis; contact dermatitis; blindness; cancer; death; very toxic to aquatic organisms	Most home and beauty parlour hair dyes, eyelash dye	
PHENYLMERCURIC ACETATE	Preservative Fungicide	☹ ☹	Allergic reactions; skin irritation; very toxic internally; very toxic to aquatic organisms; bioaccumulates in the food chain eg water organisms, fish, crustacea, birds	Mascara, shampoos	Paint
PHTHALATES (chemical compounds used in making PVC plastics; cosmetics; pesticides etc)	Film former Solvent	☹ ☹	Kidney, reproductive, liver, endocrine and neurotoxicity; mutagen; carcinogenic; teratogenic; endodrine disruption; hazardous in the environment	Nail polish, hair spray, soaps , shampoos	Production of PVC plastics, pesticides

Names	Functions	Code	Potential Effects	Cosmetic Uses	Other Uses
PIPERONAL (purple diazo dye made from oxidation of piperic acid)	Additive Flavouring	☹	Skin rash; skin irritation; CNS depression; marking of the lips; on NIH hazards list	Soaps, lipsticks, perfumes	Flavourings in foods, cigarettes
POLYACRYLAMIDE (polymer of acrylamide monomers)	Thickener Film former	☹	CNS paralysis; highly toxic and irritating to skin; can be absorbed through the skin	Moisturising cream, nail polish, tanning cream, makeup	Adhesives, plastics, pesticides
POLYETHYLENE (may be contaminated with the carcinogen 1,4-dioxane)	Binder Antistatic Stabiliser	😐 ?	No known skin toxicity; large doses caused cancer in rats; ingestion of large doses can cause liver & kidney damage	Hand lotions, skin fresheners, suntan products, underarm deodorants	Chewing gum, sheets for packaging
POLYETHYLENE GLYCOLS (may be contaminated with the carcinogen 1,4-dioxane)	Binder Solvent	☹	Skin and eye irritation; kidney and immunotoxicity; may contain traces of lead and arsenic	Barrier cream, lipstick, antiperspirant, baby products	Pharmaceutical ointments, oven cleaners
POLYOXYETHYLENE COMPOUNDS	Emulsifier	☹	Can cause sensitivity reactions; eye and skin irritation; may be contaminated with the carcinogen 1,4-dioxane	Hand cream, hand lotion	Air freshener
POLYPROPYLENE GLYCOL	Humectant	☹	*See Propylene Glycol*	Liquid makeup	Pesticides
POTASSIUM BROMATE (on Canadian Hotlist)	Antiseptic Astringent	☹	Inflamed and bleeding gums; skin and eye irritation; nausea; very toxic when ingested	Toothpaste, mouthwash, gargle	Improving additive in bread

Names	Functions	Code	Potential Effects	Cosmetic Uses	Other Uses
POTASSIUM CARBONATE (inorganic salt of potassium)	Buffer	😐 ?	Can cause dermaitis of the scalp, forehead and hands	Freckle lotions, shampoos, soaps	
POTASSIUM CHLORATE (synthetic)	Oxidising agent	☹	Gum inflammation; dermatitis; intestinal and kidney irritation; may be absorbed	Toothpaste, freckle lotions, mouthwash, gargle	Bleach, fire-works, pest-icides, matches
POTASSIUM HYDROXIDE (caustic potash)	Emulsifier Buffer	😐 ?	Skin irritation andnail damage in cuticle removers; may cause skin rash and burning; hazardous to water organisms	Liquid soap, barrier cream, hand lotion, cuticle removers	Household cleaners, button batteries
POTATO STARCH (flour prepared from potatoes)	Emollient	☺	Generally regarded as safe; may cause allergic skin reactions and stuffy nose	Dry shampoos, baby powders, dusting powders	
PPG COMPOUNDS EG PPG-5-LAURETH-5	Various	☹	*See Propylene Glycol and Ethylene Oxide*	Cosmetics	
PROPYLENE GLYCOL (synthetic; from petroleum)	Humectant Solvent	☹	Contact dermatitis; lactic acid-osis; skin rashes; dry skin; respiratory, immuno and neurotoxicity; delayed contact allergy; increased absorption of other substances	Foundation creams, mascaras, lipsticks, baby lotions, suntan lotions, cold cream	Foods, cigarettes, pesticides, antifreeze

Names	Functions	Code	Potential Effects	Cosmetic Uses	Other Uses
PROPYLENE GLYCOL ALGINATE	Stabiliser Binder	😐 ?	*See Propylene Glycol Alginate (405) in section 1*	Cosmetics	Foods
PROPYLPARABEN (propyl-p-hydroxybenzoate; synthetic)	Preservative	☹	Skin irritation and allergic reactions; contact dermatitis; photosensitivity; on NIH hazards list; *see Parabens*	Shampoos, beauty masks, nail cream, foundation creams, baby creams	Foods
PSORALEN (derived from a plant)	UV absorber	😐 ?	Photodermatitis; photosens-itivity	Sunscreens, perfumes	Treatment of vitiligo
PUMICE (lightweight porous volcanic rock)	Abrasive cleanser	☺	Generally regarded as safe; can cause irritation on dry sensitive skin	Toothpaste, hand cleansing pastes, skin cleansers	
PYCNOGENOL (blend of bioflavonoids)	Antioxidant	☺☺	Considered to have beneficial effects on health	Anti-aging products	Chewing gum, supplements
PYROCATECHOL (coal tar derivative; on Canadian Hotlist)	Antiseptic Oxidizer	☹	Contact dermatitis; eczema; kidney and liver toxicity; carcinogenic	Hair dyes, blonde-type dyes, skin care preparations	Photography, dying furs
PYROGALLOL (a phenol; on Canadian Hotlist)	Antiseptic Colouring	☹	Skin sensitisation; skin rash; ingestion can cause kidney and liver damage; circulatory collapse; mutagen; teratogen; harmful to aquatic organisms	Permanent hair dye, skin care preparations	Antimicrobial, soothing irritated skin

Names	Functions	Code	Potential Effects	Cosmetic Uses	Other Uses
QUATERNARY AMMONIUM COMPOUNDS (QUATS; synthetic derivatives of ammonium chloride)	Various	😐 ?	All QUATS can be toxic depending on dose and concentration; contact dermatitis; eye and mucous membrane irritation; serious hypersensitivity and anaphylactic shock rarely	Aerosol deodorant, antiperspirant, hand cream, mouthwash, shampoo, lipstick, after-shave lotion	Medical sterilization of mucous membranes, all-purpose cleaner
QUATERNIUM-15 (may break down to, or release formaldehyde)	Preservative	☹	Contact dermatitis; allergic reactions; eye irritation; skin rash; sensitisation	Cosmetics, shampoo, hair conditioner	
QUATERNIUM-26 (may be contaminated with pesticides and DEA)	Surfactant Antistatic agent	☹	Eye irritation; contact dermatitis; carcinogenic; *see Diethanolamine (DEA)*	Products giving sheen to hair	
QUATERNIUM-18HECTORITE	Viscosity controller	😐 ?	*See Quaternary Ammonium Compounds and Hectorite*	Skin care products, suntan gels	
QUERCETIN (type of bioflavonoid)	Colourant Antioxidant	☺	Considered to have beneficial health effects; may cause allergic reactions; on NIH hazards list; teratogenic	Dark brown shades of hair dyes	Food additives, dyeing artificial hairpieces, supplements
QUILLAJA EXTRACT (extract from the bark of a tree in South America)	Surfactant	☺	Generally regarded as safe; large oral doses are toxic; may cause local irritation	Shampoos, skin cleansers, soaps	Flavours for foods and beverages

Names	Functions	Code	Potential Effects	Cosmetic Uses	Other Uses
QUININE (alkaloid from the bark of a South American tree)	Anaesthetic Flavouring	😐 ?	Large or long-term dosages can cause headaches, skin rashes, intestinal cramps, tinnitus; cardiovascular and liver toxicity; teratogenic	Hair tonics, sunscreen preparations	Tonic water, 'bitter lemon' drinks, cold and headache remedies
QUINOLINE (coal tar derivative; may be of **ANIMAL** origin)	Solvent Colourant	☹	Psoriasis; dermatitis; gastro-intestinal, liver, respiratory and neurotoxicity; carcinogenic; may be hazardous to the environment, especially fish	Manufacture of cosmetic dyes	Preservative for anatomical specimens
RESORCINOL (derived from resins or may be synthetic)	Preservative Antiseptic Hair dye	☹	Eye and eyelid inflammation; dizziness; restlessness; endocrine disruptor; immuno, liver, cardiovascular, neurotoxicity; harmful to aquatic organisms	Antidandruff shampoos, hair dye, lipsticks, hair tonic	Tanning, explosives, printing textiles
RETINOL (Vitamin A; may be of **ANIMAL** origin; on Canadian Hotlist)	Preservative Additive	☺	Considered to have beneficial health effects; excess levels can cause yellow skin, birth defects and liver toxicity	Massage creams and oils, skin care preparations	Topical acne treatments
RETINYL PALMITATE (ester of vitamin A; may be of **ANIMAL** origin; on Canadian Hotlist)	Texturiser Additive	☺	Considered to have beneficial health effects; safe in cosmetic use up to 1% concentration; contact dermatitis	Cosmetic creams, shaving creams; makeup; suntan products	

Names	Functions	Code	Potential Effects	Cosmetic Uses	Other Uses
RICE STARCH (from pulverised rice grains; may be **GM**)	Emollient	😐 ?	Allergic reactions; can clog skin pores inhibiting proper skin function; acne	Baby powders, face powders	Foods
RICINOLEAMIDE DEA (synthetic or semisynthetic)	Antistatic agent	☹	Can contain DEA; *see Diethanolamine*	Cosmetics	
RICINOLEIC ACID (from castor beans)	Emollient Emulsifier	😐 ?	Allergic reactions; dermatitis; on NIH hazards list	Soaps, lipsticks	Contraceptive jelly
ROSE HIPS OIL (from rose hips)	Botanical	☺ ☺	Considered to have beneficial effects on the skin	Skin creams, sun care products	Natural food flavouring
ROSEMARY EXTRACT (from an evergreen shrub)	Fragrance Flavouring	☺	Considered to have beneficial health effects; may cause photosensitivity	Bubble baths, skin creams, shampoos	Natural food flavouring
ROSIN (obtained from pine trees)	Viscosity control	😐 ?	May cause contact allergies; eyelid dermatitis; asthma	Soaps, mascaras, wax depilatories	Chewing gum, varnishes
ROYAL BEE JELLY (of **ANIMAL** origin)	Biological additive	☺	Considered by some reseachers to have beneficial health effects	Cosmetics	
SAFFRON (dried stigma of the crocus plant)	Colouring Flavouring	☺	Generally regarded as safe; may have beneficial health effects; anaphylaxis	Perfumery, cosmetics	Flavour in food and beverages, marking ink

Names	Functions	Code	Potential Effects	Cosmetic Uses	Other Uses
SAFROLE (toxic component of volatile oils such as nutmeg and star anise; on Canadian Hotlist)	Fragrance Flavouring	☹☹	Liver, kidney, reproductive and neurotoxicity; on NIH hazards list; carcinogenic; teratogenic	Cheap soaps and perfumes	Beverage flavouring?
SALICYLATES (salts of salicylic acid-benzyl, amyl, methyl, phenyl; found in fruits and vegetables)	Flavouring	😐?	Allergic reactions in people sensitive to aspirin; hyperactivity; kidney, cardiovascular and neurotoxicity; asthma	*See Methyl Salicylate*	Ice cream, jam, cake mixes, chewing gum, antiseptics
SALICYLIC ACID (may be derived by heating phenol with carbon dioxide; one of the beta hydroxy acids; on Canadian Hotlist)	Preservative Antiseptic	☹	Large amounts absorbed can cause vomiting, abdominal pain, acidosis and skin rash; allergic reactions; dermatitis; teratogenic; aspirin-sensitive people should avoid	Skin softener, face masks, make-up, hair dye remover, deodorant, suntan lotion	Food products, fungicide, topical treatment for acne
SARCOSINES AND SARCOSINATES (found in starfish and sea urchins or formed from caffeine; may be of **ANIMAL** origin)	Surfactant	😐?	Non-irritating and non-sensitising; can cause formation of nitrosamines; can enhance penetration of other ingredients through the skin; *see Nitrosamines*	Shampoos, soaps, dentifrices, lubricating oils	Dishwashing liquids
SASSAFRAS OIL (volatile oil from sassafras plant; 80% safrole)	Fragrance Flavouring	😐?	Dermatitis in sensitive people; unsafe in foods unless safrole-free; *see Safrole*	Perfumes, soaps, dentrifices	Flavouring in foods, topical antiseptic

Names	Functions	Code	Potential Effects	Cosmetic Uses	Other Uses
SELENIUM SULPHIDE (on Canadian Hotlist)	Antidandruff agent	☹	Skin irritation; dryness of hair & scalp; liver toxicity; severe eye irritation; carcinogenic	Medicated antidandruff shampoo	Treatment for tinea versicolour
SHEA BUTTER (from fruit of the karite tree)	Emollient Emulsifier	☺☺	Softens and moisturises skin; no known toxicity	Moisturiser, lipstick, lip balm, suntan gel	
SILVER NITRATE	Hair dye	☹	Poisonous; caustic & irritating; skin sensitivity; allergies; very toxic to aquatic organisms	Metallic hair dyes	
SODIUM ALPHA-OLEFIN SULFONATES	Cleanser	😐?	May cause eye and skin irritation and sensitisation; foetal abnormalities in animals	Shampoos, bath and shower products	
SODIUM CARBONATE (soda ash)	Buffer Oxidising agent	😐?	Breathing difficulty, abdominal pain, collapse from ingestion; liver toxicity; can cause scalp, forehead & hand rash	Shampoos, vaginal douches, soaps, permanent wave solutions, bath salts	Dishwashing liquid, cigarettes, pesticides
SODIUM CHLORIDE (common table salt)	Preservative Viscosity control	😐?	Can beirritating and corrosive to skin & mucous membranes; dry skin; skin rash; teratogenic	Shampoos, liquid hand wash, bubble baths, mouthwash	Butter, meats, cigarettes
SODIUM COCOYL SARCOSINATE (may be of **ANIMAL** origin)	Surfactant	😐?	*See Sarcosines*	Shampoo, hand and body wash	

Names	Functions	Code	Potential Effects	Cosmetic Uses	Other Uses
SODIUM COCOYL ISETHIONATE	Surfactant	☺	Considered safe in cosmetic use; mild skin & eye irritation	Bar soaps, body wash, skin scrubs	
SODIUM FLUORIDE (on Canadian Hotlist)	Preservative Oral care	☹ ☹	*See Fluoride*	Cosmetics, tooth-pastes, dentifrices	Cigarettes
SODIUM HYDROXIDE (caustic soda)	Emulsifier Alkali	😐 ?	Dermatitis of the scalp; ingest-ion can cause vomiting, hypo-tension, diarrhoea & collapse; may be hazardous to the environment, especially water organisms	Shampoos, soaps, hair straighteners, liquid face powders	Pesticides
SODIUM HYDROXYMETHYL GLYCINATE	Preservative	😐 ?	May release formaldehyde; NIH could not locate any studies for safety	Cosmetics	
SODIUM LAURAMINOPROPIONATE	Surfactant Antistatic	☺	Mild reactions in sensitive people	Shampoo, hair conditioner	
SODIUM LAURETH SULPHATE (may contain carcinogens 1,4-dioxane and ethylene oxide)	Surfactant Detergent	☹	Mild eye and skin irritation; can cause the formation of nitrosamines; toxic to aquatic organisms; *see Nitrosamines*	Shampoo, tooth-paste, bath gel, bubble bath, liquid hand & body wash	Dishwashing liquid
SODIUM LAUROYL SARCOSINATE (may be of **ANIMAL** origin)	Surfactant Antistatic agent	😐 ?	*See Sarcosines*	Hair conditioners	

Names	Functions	Code	Potential Effects	Cosmetic Uses	Other Uses
SODIUM LAURYL SULPHATE (may be prepared synthetically by sulfation of lauryl alcohol then neutralization with sodium carbonate)	Surfactant Denaturant Emulsifier	☹	Skin, eye and mucous membrane irritation; dry skin; eczema; mouth ulcers; liver and gastrointestinal toxicity; on NIH hazards list; teratogen; toxic to aquatic organisms	Bubble baths, hair conditioners, liquid hand & body wash, shampoos, toothpastes, moisturiser	Cake mix, dried egg products, marshmallows, industrial cleaning products
SODIUM LAURYL SULPHOACETATE	Surfactant	☺	Mild to strong skin irritation; slight eye irritation; slightly toxic to rats in oral doses	Cream shampoos, cleansing creams, bath bombs	
SODIUM METHYL COCOYL TAURATE (of **ANIMAL** origin, ox bile)	Emulsifier Surfactant	😐?	May cause formation of nitrosamines; *see Nitrosamines*	Cosmetics	
SODIUM MYRETH SULPHATE (may be of **ANIMAL** origin)	Emulsifier	☺	Mild to moderate eye irritation in animal studies	Shampoos	
SODIUM MYRISTOYL SARCOSINATE (may be of **ANIMAL** origin)	Surfactant Antistatic	😐?	*See Sarcosines*	Moisturiser s	
SODIUM C14-C16 OLEFIN SULFONATE	Surfactant	😐?	May cause skin irritation; hair dryness and denaturing; may cause nitrosamine formation	Cosmetics, hair conditioner, shampoo	

Names	Functions	Code	Potential Effects	Cosmetic Uses	Other Uses
SODIUM OLETH SULPHATE (may be of **ANIMAL** origin)	Emulsifier	☹	May be contaminated with ethylene oxide and/or 1,4-dioxane *(see both)*	Cosmetics	
SODIUM SILICATE (water glass)	Anticaking agent	😐?	Can cause skin and mucous membrane irritation; vomiting and diarrhoea when ingested	Barrier creams, soaps, depilatories	Preserving eggs, laundry detergent
SODIUM STEARATE (may be of **ANIMAL** origin)	Emulsifier Surfactant	☺	Nonirritating to the skin; safety is under review	Toothpastes, soap-less shampoos, shaving lather	
SORBITAN LAURATE	Emulsifier	☺	Generally recognised as safe; may cause contact urticaria	Cosmetic creams and lotions	Foods
SORBITAN OLEATE (may be of **ANIMAL** origin)	Emulsifier Plasticiser	😐?	Generally recognised as safe; may cause contact urticaria and allergic reactions	Cosmetics, eye shadow	
SORBITAN PALMITATE (may be of ANIMAL origin)	Emulsifier	☺	Generally recognised as safe; may cause contact dermatitis	Shampoo, hair conditioner, cosmetic creams	
SORBITAN STEARATE (may be of ANIMAL origin)	Emulsifier	☺	Generally recognised as safe; may cause contact urticaria	Shampoo, suntan lotion, deodorant, toothpaste, soap	

Names	Functions	Code	Potential Effects	Cosmetic Uses	Other Uses
SORBITOL (may be synthetic)	Humectant	☺	Considered nontoxic when used on the skin	Shampoos, toothpaste, hand lotions	*See Sorbitol (420) section 1*
SOYBEAN OIL (soyabean oil; may be **GM**)	Emollient	😐 ?	Goiter from excess consumption; flatulence; indigestion; allergic reactions; pimples; hair damage in topical use	Soaps, shampoos, moisturisers, bath oils	Soy sauce, margarine, soy products
SOYTRIMONIUM CHLORIDE (likely to be **GM**)	Preservative Emulsifier	😐 ?	*See Quaternary Ammonium Compounds*	Cosmetics	
SPEARMINT OIL (oil of spearmint)	Fragrance Flavouring	☺	Considered to have beneficial health effects; may cause skin rash	Perfumes, toothpaste, perfumed cosmetics	Chewing gum, cigarettes
SPERMACETI (of **ANIMAL** origin, from sperm whales)	Emollient	☺	Considered nontoxic but may become rancid and cause skin irritation	Shampoos, cold creams	
SQUALANE (may be of **ANIMAL** origin (shark liver oil))	Lubricant Emollient	☺☺	Generally considered safe in cosmetic use	Skin and hair cosmetics	
SQUALENE (may be of **ANIMAL** origin (shark liver oil))	Emollient Antistatic	☺☺	Considered to have beneficial health effects	Skin care products, hair dyes, fixative in perfumes	Shark liver oil, supplements

Names	Functions	Code	Potential Effects	Cosmetic Uses	Other Uses
STARCH (unmodified; found in many plants; may be **GM**)	Thickener	😐 ?	Poorly digested; when used in cosmetic products acne; dermatitis; hayfever	Dusting powders, baby powders, dry shampoos	Processed foods
STARCH - MODIFIED (starch treated with sodium hydroxide, propylene oxide, aluminium sulphate and others; may be **GM**)	Thickener Binder	😐 ?	Safety concern about bodies resistance to chemicals used to modify starch esp babies; diarrhoea in babies; when used in cosmetic products acne; dermatitis; hayfever	Cosmetic products	Processed foods, baby foods, cigarettes
STANNOUS FLUORIDE (solution of tin in hydrofluoric acid; on Canadian Hotlist)	Oral care agent	☹ ☹	*See Fluoride*	Dentifrices	
STEARALKONIUM CHLORIDE (may be of **ANIMAL** origin)	Preservative	☹	Mild skin irritation; severe eye irritation; dermatitis; may contain DEA; *see Quaternary Ammonium Compounds and Diethanolamine*	Hair conditioners	
STEARAMIDE DEA (may be of **ANIMAL** origin)	Opacifier Antistatic	☹	DEA -related ingredient; *see Diethanolamine*	Shampoo, hair conditioner	
STEARAMIDE MEA (may be of **ANIMAL** origin)	Opacifier Antistatic	☹	DEA -related ingredient; *see Diethanolamine*	Shampoo, hair conditioner	

Names	Functions	Code	Potential Effects	Cosmetic Uses	Other Uses
STEARAMIDOPROPYL BETAINE (may be of **ANIMAL** origin)	Antistatic agent	😐 ?	*See Quaternary Ammonium Compounds*	Hair conditioners	
STEARAMIDOPROPYL DIMETHYLAMINE (may be of **ANIMAL** origin)	Emulsifier Antistatic agent	😐 ?	Allergic dermatitis; may promote the formation of nitrosamines; *see Nitrosamines*	Hair conditioners	
STEARIC ACID (may be of **ANIMAL** origin)	Emulsifier Anticaking agent	😐 ?	May cause allergic reactions in people with sensitive skin; health effects not adequately investigated	Deodorants, hand creams, barrier creams, soaps	Chewing gum base, suppositories
STEAROYL SARCOSINE (may be of **ANIMAL** origin)	Antistatic agent	😐 ?	*See Sarcosines*	Shaving gel	
STEARYL ALCOHOL (of **ANIMAL** origin)	Emollient Opacifier	☺	May cause allergic reactions and contact dermatitis in people with sensitive skin	Depilatories, hair rinse, moisturisers, shampoos	Pharmaceuticals
STEVIA & STEVIOSIDE (Brazilian herb and extract; banned in some countries)	Oral care agent	☺	No adverse effects reported in humans, some reports of adverse reactions in animals	Toothpastes, dental care products	Dietary supplements
STYRENE (derived from ethylbenzene)	Binder	☹	Liver, blood, endocrine, kidney and neurotoxicity; teratogenic; carcinogenic	Manufacture of cosmetic resins	Chewing gum, manufacture of plastics

Names	Functions	Code	Potential Effects	Cosmetic Uses	Other Uses
STYRENE/PVP COPOLOMER (from vinyl pyrrolidone andstyrene monomers)	Film former Opacifier	☹	*See Styrene and Polyvinylpyrrolodone*	Liquid eyeliners	
SULPHITES (sodium, potassium and ammonium)	Preservative Antioxidant	☹	Asthma; anaphylactic shock; skin rash; nausea; stomach irritation; diarrhoea; swelling; destroy vitamin B1	Hair waves, hair dyes, artificial tanning products,	Various foods and beverages, cellophane for food packaging
SULFONAMIDE (sulfanilamide; on Canadian Hotlist)	Antibiotic	☹	Itching; skin rash; swelling; hives; kidney toxicity; terat-ogenic; on NIH hazards list	Cosmetics, nail polish	Antibiotic to treat bacterial & fungal infections
SUPER OXIDE DISMUTASE (an antioxidant enzyme found in the body)	Biological additive Antioxidant	☺☺	Considered to have benefic-ial effects when applied to the skin	Hair care products, skin creams	Encapsulated and injectable pharmaceuticals
TALC (naturally occuring mineral)	Anticaking agent Absorbent	☹	Lung irritation; pneumonia; cough; vomiting; ovarian and lung cancer; carcinogenic	Face creams, baby powders, eye shadows	
TALCUM POWDER (may contain boric acid)	Absorbent	☹	*See Talc*	*See Talc*	
TEA COMPOUNDS	Various	☹	*See Triethanolamine*	Personal care and cosmetic products	

Names	Functions	Code	Potential Effects	Cosmetic Uses	Other Uses
TEA LAURYL SULPHATE	Surfactant	☹	*See Triethanolamine and Sodium Lauryl Sulphate*	Hair care products, mudpacks	
TERPINEOL	Flavouring Denaturant Solvent	☹	Pneumonitis; eye and mucous membrane irritation; on NIH hazards list; CNS depression	Perfume, hairspray, soap, after-shave, roll-on deodorant	Bleach, laundry detergent, cigarettes
TERTIARY BUTYLHYDROQUINONE (on Canadian Hotlist)	Antioxidant	☹	Allergic reactions; contact dermatitis; birth defects in animals; carcinogenic	Cosmetics; lipsticks, eye shadows	Foods
TETRABROMOFLUORESCEIN	Colourant	☹	Photosensitivity; inflammation of lips; respiratory and gastrointestinal symptoms	Indelible lipsticks, nail polish	Dyeing of wool, silk and paper
THEOBROMA OIL (derived from cacao bean)	Emollient Botanical	☺	Allergic reactions in some people; acne	Soaps, cosmetics	Confectionery, pharmaceuticals
THEOBROMINE (alkaloid closely related to caffeine)	Botanical	😐 ?	Stimulates the CNS; atrophy of the testicles; endocrine, liver & neurotoxicity; teratogen	Skin conditioner in cosmetics	Chocolate, blood vessel dilator
THIMEROSAL (mercury; on Canadian Hotlist)	Preservative	☹ ☹	Allergic reactions; contact dermatitis; *see Mercury Compounds*	Eye preparations	Filler in vaccines

Names	Functions	Code	Potential Effects	Cosmetic Uses	Other Uses
THIOUREA (made by heating a derivative of ammonium cyanide; on Canadian Hotlist)	Preservative Additive	☹☹	Skin irritation; allergic reactions; cardiovascular; immuno & reproductive toxicity; carcinogenic; on NIH hazards list; toxic to aquatic organisms	Hair dye, hair preparations, cosmetics	Photography, dyes, wet suits, silver polish
THYMOL (obtained from essential oil of lavender and others)	Additive Fragrance	😐?	Allergic reactions; ingestion can cause nausea, vomiting, dizziness; neurotoxicity	Cosmetics, after shave, mouthwash	Food flavouring
TITANIUM DIOXIDE (occurs naturally; may contain nanoparticles)	Colouring Opacifier	😐?	*See Titanium Dioxide (171) in section 1; see also Nanoparticles*	Sunscreens, bath powders, barrier creams	Colouring on foods, paints, marker ink
TOLUENE (derived from petroleum or by distilling Tolu balsam, a plant extract)	Solvent	☹☹	Cardiovascular, respiratory, kidney, liver, developmental, reproductive, neuro and immunotoxicity; eye and skin irritation; decreased learning ability; brain damage; toxic to aquatic organisms	Hair gel, perfumes, nail polishs, hair spray, hair dyes	Removing odours in cheese, metal cleaner, glue
TOLUENE-2, 5-DIAMINE (on Canadian Hotlist)	Hair dye	☹☹	Harmful to aquatic organisms; see *Toluene*	Hair dyes	
TOLUENE-3, 4-DIAMINE	Hair dye	☹☹	Harmful to aquatic organisms; see *Toluene*	Hair dyes	Dyes for furs, textiles, leather

Names	Functions	Code	Potential Effects	Cosmetic Uses	Other Uses
TRETINOIN (retinoic acid from vitamin A; may be of **ANIMAL** origin)	Skin improver	😐 ?	Considered to have beneficial health effects; may cause skin peeling, chapping, blistering and swelling	Antiwrinkle creams, 'anti-ageing' creams	Acne treatments
TRIBROMOSALAN (on Canadian Hotlist)	Antiseptic Fungicide	☹	Prohibited in cosmetics in the USA in 2000 as it may cause photoallergies	Soaps, medicated cosmetics	
TRICHLOROETHANE (methyl chloroform)	Solvent Degreaser	☹☹	Severe mucous membrane & eye irritation; liver, neuro & cardiovascular toxicity; cardiac arrest; vomiting; teratogen; harmful to aquatic organisms	Cosmetics, nail polish	Correction fluid, degreaser, glue, spot remover, detergent
TRICLOCARBAN (prepared from analine, a benzene derivative)	Preservative	☹	Photoallergic reactions; convulsions; prolonged use may cause cancer	Soaps, medicated cosmetics, deodorant	
TRICLOSAN (may contain toxic chemicals; on Canadian Hotlist)	Preservative	☹	Allergic reactions; contact dermatitis; toxic by ingestion; liver damage in animals	Antiperspirants, deodorant soaps mouthwash	Household products, drugs
TRIETHANOLAMINE (TEA)	Buffer Coating additive	☹	Allergic contact dermatitis; skin irritation; may react with nitrites to form nitrosamines; on NIH hazards list	Hand and body lotion, hair conditioner, 'no rinse' shampoo	Coating on fresh fruit and vegetables, detergents

Names	Functions	Code	Potential Effects	Cosmetic Uses	Other Uses
TRISODIUM PHOSPHATE (from phosphate rock)	Buffer Chelating agent	😐 ?	Can cause skin irritation; neurotoxicity	Shampoos, bubble baths, cuticle softeners	Additive in foods, pesticides
UREA (found in urine; may be of **ANIMAL** origin; may be synthetic; on Canadian Hotlist)	Humectant Antistatic agent	😐 ?	Thinning of the epidermis; allergic reactions in some people; dermatitis; alleviates dry skin	Skin creams and lotions, mouthwash, moisturiser	Browning agent in baked goods like pretzels, cigarettes
VANILLIN (made from eugenol or waste from the wood pulp industry)	Additive Flavouring	😐 ?	Skin irritation; eczema; skin pigmentation; contact dermatitis; on NIH hazards list	Perfumes	Chocolate, cheese, candy, cigarettes
WAXES (from petroleum, animals, plants and insects; can contain pesticides; may be of **ANIMAL** origin)	Film former Emollient	😐 ?	Generally safe in cosmetic use; may cause allergic reactions depending on source and purity	Cosmetics, hair-grooming preparations, lipsticks, hair straighteners	Coatings on fresh fruit and vegetables, packaging materials
WINTERGREEN OIL	Flavouring Denaturant	☹	Harmful to aquatic organisms; see *Methyl Salicylate*	*See Methyl Salicylate*	*See Methyl Salicylate*
YUCCA EXTRACT (derived from a plant grown in southwestern USA)	Foaming agent Botanical	😊 😊	Considered to have beneficial health effects	Shampoos, organic cosmetics	Root beer flavouring

Names	Functions	Code	Potential Effects	Cosmetic Uses	Other Uses
ZINC CHLORIDE (soluble zinc salt)	Oral care agent	☹	Toxic; mild skin irritation; contact dermatitis; can be absorbed through the skin; teratogenic; very toxic to aquatic organisms	Mouthwash, dentrifices	Pesticides
ZINC MYRISTATE (zinc salt of myristic acid)	Opacifier Viscosity control	😐 ?	Toxic; may promote acne; nausea and vomiting if ingested	Makeup, nail polish	
ZINC OXIDE (may contain nanoparticles)	Opacifier Additive Colouring	😐 ?	Helps protect against UV radiation; may be unsuitable for dry skin; respiratory toxicity; may cause skin eruptions; teratogenic; *see Nanoparticles*	Baby powder, antiperspirant, shaving cream, calamine lotion, sunscreen, hair products	Used medically as an antiseptic, astringent and protective in skin diseases
ZINC STEARATE (may be of **ANIMAL** origin)	Colouring	😐 ?	Skin and eye irritation; lung problems and pneumonitis	Baby powder, hand cream, face powder	Tablet manufacture
ZINC SULPHATE (from reaction of zinc and sulphuric acid)	Anti-microbial	😐 ?	Skin and mucous membrane irritation; allergic reactions; cardiovascular toxicity	Skin tonics, eye lotions, aftershave, shaving creams	Paperboard products
ZIRCONIUM (banned in aerosol cosmetic products in the USA; on Canadian Hotlist)	Solvent Abrasive	😐 ?	Considered safe in non-aerosol products; toxic by inhalation; respiratory toxicity; contact allergic reactions	Cosmetic cream, antiperspirant, deodorant	Preparation of dyes

Names	Functions	Code	Potential Effects	Cosmetic Uses	Other Uses

Glossary

ABRASIVE: A substance added to cosmetic products either to remove materials from various body surfaces or to aid mechanical tooth cleaning and improve gloss.

ABSORBENT: A substance added to cosmetic products to take up water and/or oil-soluble dissolved or finely dispersed substances.

ACETYLATED: An organic compound that has had its water removed by heating with acetic anhydride or acetyl chloride. Both these chemicals are hazardous.

ADDITIVE: A substance added to cosmetic products, often in relatively small amounts, to impart or improve desirable properties or minimise undesirable properties.

ALLERGEN: Any substance capable of provoking an inappropriate immune response in susceptible people, but not normally in others.

ALLERGIC CONTACT DERMATITIS: A skin rash caused by direct contact with a substance to which the skin is sensitive. Symptoms may occur anywhere from seven days to many years after repeated low-level exposures, as occurs with cosmetics and personal care products.

ALLERGIC REACTION: An adverse immune system response involving unusual sensitivity to the action of various environmental stimuli. These stimuli do not normally cause symptoms in the majority of the population.

AMINES: A class of organic compounds derived from ammonia.

ANTICAKING AGENT: A substance used in granular foods like salt or flour to assist free flowing.

ANTICORROSIVE: Chemicals added to cosmetics to prevent corrosion of the packaging or the machinery used in the manufacture of the cosmetic.

ANTIFOAMING AGENT: A substance added to foods or cosmetics to prevent excessive frothing or foaming, reduce the formation of scum or prevent boiling over during manufacture.

ANTIMICROBIAL: A substance added to a cosmetic product to help reduce the activities of micro-organisms on the skin or body.

ANTIOXIDANT: A substance added to foods or cosmetics to prevent changes or spoiling due to exposure to air. May be natural or synthetic.

ANTISTATIC: A substance used to reduce static electricity by neutralising electrical charge on a surface.

AZO DYES: A very large class of dyes made from diazonium compounds and phenol. Many azo dyes are thought to be carcinogenic when used in foods.

BINDER: A substance added to a solid cosmetic mixture to provide cohesion.

BIOLOGICAL ADDITIVE: A substance, derived from a biological origin, added to a cosmetic product to achieve a specific formulation feature.

BLEACHING AGENT: A substance used to artificially bleach and whiten flour. A substance used in a cosmetic product to lighten the shade of hair or skin.

BOTANICAL: A substance, derived from plants, added to a cosmetic product to achieve a specific formulation feature.

BUFFER: A substance added to a food or cosmetic product to adjust, maintain or stabilise the acid/alkali (pH) balance.

CANADIAN HOTLIST: Information about cosmetic ingredients that have the potential for adverse effect or which have been restricted or banned.

CARCINOGEN: A cancer-causing substance. IARC and NTP list carcinogens in 3 categories. 1 = confirmed human carcinogen; 2 = probable human carcinogen; 3 = possible human carcinogen.

CARCINOGENIC: A substance that is capable of causing cancer.

CARDIOVASCULAR/BLOOD TOXICITY: Adverse effects on the cardiovascular or hematopoietic systems that result from exposure to chemical substances. Exposure can contribute to a variety of diseases; including elevated blood pressure (hypertension), hardening of the arteries (arteriosclerosis), abnormal heartbeat (cardiac arrhythmia) and decreased blood flow to the heart (coronary ischemia). Exposure can also reduce the oxygen carrying capacity of red blood cells, disrupt important immunological processes carried out by white blood cells and induce cancer.

CHELATING AGENT: A substance added to a food or cosmetic product to react and form complexes with metal ions that could affect stability and/or appearance.

CIR EXPERT PANEL: A body set up in 1976 by the Cosmetic, Toiletry and Fragrance Association to review the safety of ingredients used in cosmetics.

CLARIFYING AGENT: A substance that removes small amounts of suspended particles from liquids.

CNS: Central Nervous System - our body's major communication network.

COAL TAR DYE: Dyes that were once made from coal tar but are now commercially produced by a synthetic process. These dyes are extremely complex chemical compounds, which have had inadequate testing and often contain toxic impurities.

CONTACT DERMATITIS: *See allergic contact dermatitis.*

COSMETIC ACNE: Acne caused by applying cosmetics to the skin.

CYTOTOXIN: A substance that is poisonous to cells.

DENATURANT: A poisonous or unpleasant substance added to alcoholic cosmetics to prevent them being ingested. It is also a substance that changes the natural qualities or characteristics of other substances.

DEPILATORY: A substance or agent used to remove unwanted body hair.

DERMATITIS: Inflammation of the skin with pain, redness, burning or itching and fluid build-up.

DEVELOPMENTAL TOXICITY: Adverse effects on the developing foetus that result from exposure to chemical substances. Developmental toxicants, sometimes called teratogens, include agents that induce structural malformations and other birth defects, low birth weight, metabolic or biological dysfunction and psychological or behavioural deficits that become manifest as the child grows.

DILUENT: A substance used to dilute or dissolve other additives.

DPIM: "Dangerous Properties of Industrial Materials." Ed. Sax & Lewis.

ECZEMA: Wet or dry inflammation of the skin causing redness, pain, itching, scaling, peeling, blistering etc.

EDF: Environmental Defense; provides information on chemicals.

EMOLLIENT: A substance used to soften and soothe the skin.

EMULSIFIER: A substance used in food or cosmetic products to stabilise mixtures and ensure consistency.

EMULSION STABILISER: A substance added to a cosmetic product to help the process of emulsification and to improve formulation stability and shelf life.

ENDOCRINE TOXICITY: Adverse effects on the structure and/or functioning of the endocrine system that result from exposure to chemical substances. The endocrine system is composed of many organs and glands that secrete hormones directly into the bloodstream including the pituitary, hypothalamus, thyroid, adrenals, pancreas, thymus, ovaries and testes. Compounds that are toxic to the endocrine system may cause diseases such as hypothyroidism, diabetes mellitus, hypoglycaemia, reproductive disorders and cancer.

EPA: Environmental Protection Agency

ETHOXYLATION: The addition of ethyl (from the gas ethane) and oxygen to a degreasing agent to make it less abrasive and cause it to foam more.

FDA: Food and Drug Administration (USA). It is part of the Public Health Service of the US Department of Health and Human Services.

FD & C: Abbreviation for Food, Drug and Cosmetic. A listing of synthetic colours in the USA, by the Food and Drug Administration.

FILM FORMER: A substance added to a cosmetic product to produce, when applied, a continuous film on skin hair or nails.

FLAVOUR ENHANCER: Chemicals that enhance the taste or odour of food without contributing any taste or odour of their own.

FLAVOURING: The largest category of food additives. Over two thousand synthetic and natural flavourings added to foods to impart the desired flavour.

FRAGRANCE: Any natural or synthetic substance used to impart an odour to a product.

FUNGICIDE: A substance used to kill or inhibit the growth of fungi.

GELLING AGENT: A substance that is capable of forming a jelly.

GM: Abbreviation for Genetically Modified.

GMO: Genetically Modified Organism.

GLAZING AGENT: A substance used to provide a shiny appearance or a protective coat to a food.

GRAS: Generally Recognised As Safe. A list, established by American Congress in 1958, of substances added to food over a long time.

HAZARDOUS CHEMICAL AGENTS: 1.Those chemical agents known to have undesirable biological effects, either acutely or chronically, reasonable regard being given to the size of the dose, duration and type of exposure and the physical state of the compound required to produce such effects. 2.Those agents for which toxicity information is not available but are highly suspect for reasons of similarity in chemical structure or function to known toxic agents. 3.Those agents that are explosive or violently reactive.

HERBICIDE: A substance used to kill or inhibit the growth of unwanted plants.

HUMECTANT: A substance used to hold and retain moisture to prevent a food or product from drying out.

HYDROGENATED: Liquid oils in food and cosmetic products are converted to semisolid fats at room temperature by adding hydrogen under high pressure. Hydrogenated fats and oils contribute to cancer, heart disease and atheroma.

HYDROLYSED: Turned partly into water as a result of a chemical process.

IMMUNOTOXICITY: Adverse effects on the functioning of the immune system that result from exposure to chemical substances. Altered immune function may lead to the increased incidence or severity of infectious diseases or cancer, since the immune systems ability to respond adequately to invading agents is suppressed. Toxic agents can also cause autoimmune diseases, in which healthy tissue is attacked by an immune system that fails to differentiate self-antigens from foreign antigens.

INTERMEDIATE: A chemical substance found as part of a necessary step between one organic compound and another.

KIDNEY TOXICITY: Adverse effects on the kidney, ureter or bladder that result from exposure to chemical substances. Some toxic agents cause acute injury to the kidney, while others produce chronic changes that can lead to end-stage renal failure or cancer. The consequences of renal failure can be profound, sometimes resulting in permanent damage that requires dialysis or kidney transplantation.

LIVER/GASTROINTESTINAL TOXICITY: Adverse effects on the structure and/or functioning of the gastrointestinal tract, liver, or gall bladder that result from exposure to chemical substances. The liver is frequently subject to injury induced by chemicals, called hepatotoxins, because of its role as the body's principal site of metabolism.

MATERIAL SAFETY DATA SHEETS (MSDS): Data compiled by manufacturers of chemicals providing information on health hazards and safe handling procedures.

MILIARIA: Acute itchy skin condition occurring as an eruption of spots or blisters resembling millet seeds.

MODIFIER: A substance that induces or stabilises certain shades in hair colouring.

MUSCULOSKELETAL TOXICITY: Adverse effects on the structure and/or functioning of the muscles, bones and joints that result from exposure to chemical substances. Exposure to toxic substances such as coal dust and cadmium has been shown to cause adverse changes to the musculoskeletal system. The bone disorders arthritis, fluorosis and osteomalacia are among the musculoskeletal diseases that can be induced by occupational or environmental toxicants.

MUTAGEN: Any substance that induces mutation or permanent changes to genetic material (DNA) of cells.

MUTAGENIC: Capable of causing mutations. Can be induced by stimuli such as certain food chemicals, pesticides and radiation.

NANOPARTICLES: Anything smaller than 100 nanometres (a nanometre is a billionth of a metre) in size or more than 800 times smaller than a human hair. They can enter the bloodstream and cross the blood-brain barrier.

NECROSIS: Cell death.

NEUROTOXICITY: Adverse effects on the structure or functioning of the central and/or peripheral nervous system that result from exposure to chemical substances. Symptoms of neurotoxicity include muscle weakness, loss of sensation and motor control, tremors, alterations in cognition and impaired functioning of the autonomic nervous system.

NIH: National Institutes of Health. Provides a data bank of hazardous chemicals.

NIOSH: The National Institute of Occupational Safety and Health, which is the research arm of the US Occupational Safety and Health Administration (OSHA).

NITROSAMINES: Potential carcinogenic compounds formed when an amine reacts with a nitrosating agent or substances containing nitrites.

NITROSATING AGENT: A substance capable of introducing nitrogen and oxygen molecules into a compound that may cause the compound to form potential carcinogenic nitrosamines.

NRC: Not recommended for children.

NTP: National Toxicology Program (USA). Information on chemical toxicity.

OPACIFIER: A substance added to a shampoo or other transparent or translucent liquid cosmetic product to make it impervious to visible light or nearby radiation.

ORAL CARE AGENT: A substance added to a personal care product for the care of the oral cavity.

OXIDISING AGENT: A substance added to a food or cosmetic product to change the chemical nature of another substance by adding oxygen.

PHOTOALLERGY: *See photosensitivity.*

PHOTOSENSITIVITY: A condition in which the application to the body or ingestion of certain chemicals causes skin problems (rash, pigmentation changes, swelling etc) when the skin is exposed to sunlight.

PHOTOTOXICITY: Reaction to sunlight or ultraviolet light resulting in inflammation.

PLASTICISER: A substance added to impart flexibility and workability without changing the nature of a material.

PRESERVATIVE: A substance added to food and cosmetic products to inhibit the growth of bacteria, fungi and viruses.

PROPELLANT: A gas used to expel the contents of containers in the form of aerosols.

REAGENT: A substance used for the detection of another substance by chemical or microscopic means.

REDUCING AGENT: A substance added to food and cosmetic products to decrease, deoxidise or concentrate the volume of another substance.

REPRODUCTIVE TOXICITY: Adverse effects on the male and female reproductive systems that result from exposure to chemical substances. Reproductive toxicity may be expressed as alterations in sexual behaviour, decreases in fertility or loss of the foetus during pregnancy. A reproductive toxicant may interfere with the sexual functioning or reproductive ability of exposed individuals from puberty throughout adulthood.

RESPIRATORY TOXICITY: Adverse effects on the structure or functioning of the respiratory system that result from exposure to chemical substances. The respiratory system consists of the nasal passages, pharynx, trachea, bronchi and lungs. Respiratory toxicants can produce a variety of acute and chronic pulmonary conditions, including local irritation, bronchitis, pulmonary oedema, emphysema and cancer.

RTECS: The Registry of Toxic Effects of Chemical Substances.

SENSITISATION: Heightened immune response following repeated contact with an allergen.

SEQUESTRANT: A substance capable of attaching itself to unwanted trace metals such as cadmium, iron and copper that cause deterioration in food and cosmetic products by advancing the oxidation process.

SOLVENT: A substance added to food and cosmetic products to dissolve or disperse other components.

STABILISER: A substance added to a product to give it body and to maintain a desired texture.

SURFACE ACTIVE AGENT: A substance that reduces surface tension when dissolved in solution. These agents fall into three categories: detergents, wetting agents and emulsifiers.

SURFACTANT: A wetting agent that lowers the surface tension of a liquid substance allowing it to spread out and penetrate more easily. Surfactants fall into four main categories - anionic, non-ionic, cationic and amphoteric.

TENDERISER: A substance or process used to alter the structure of meat to make it less tough and more palatable.

TERATOGEN: *See developmental toxicity.*

TERATOGENIC: Capable of causing defects in a developing foetus.

TEXTURISER: A substance used to improve the texture of various foods or cosmetics.

THICKENER: A substance used to add viscosity and body to foods, lotions and creams.

UV ABSORBER: A substance added to a cosmetic product to filter ultra-violet (UV) rays so as to protect the skin or the product from the harmful effects of these rays.

VISCOSITY CONTROLLING AGENT: A substance added to a cosmetic product to increase or decrease the viscosity (flowability) of the finished product.

XENOESTROGEN: An environmental compound that has oestrogen-like activity thereby mimicking the properties of the hormone oestrogen.

Bibliography

Agency for Toxic Substances and Disease Registry, (ATSDR)
American Academy of Dermatology
Antczak, Dr Stephen & Gina, "Cosmetics Unmasked", *Thorsons,* 2001
Australian Consumers Association
Cancer Prevention Coalition
Center for Science in the Public Interest (CSPI)
Commonwealth Scientific and Industrial Research Organization (CSIRO)
Day, Phillip, "Cancer – Why We're Still Dying to Know the Truth", *Credence Publications,* 2000
Day, Phillip, "Health Wars", *Credence Publications,* 2001
Department of Food Science and Technology (UK)
Dingle, Peter and Toni Brown, "Dangerous Beauty – Cosmetics and Personal Care" *Healthy Home Solutions,* 1999
Epstein, Samuel S. M.D., "Unreasonable Risk" *Environmental Toxicology,* 2002
Environmental Defence
Environmental Protection Agency, (EPA), (USA)
Environmental Working Group
Food and Drug Administration (FDA), (USA)
Food Standards Agency (UK)
Food Standards Australia New Zealand (FSANZ)
Hampton, Aubrey, "What's in Your Cosmetics", *Organica Press*

Hanssen Maurice, with Jill Marsden, "The New Additive Code Breaker" *Lothian*, 1991
In-Tele-Health, Hyperhealth Natural Health & Nutrition CD-ROM 2005 Ed.
International Agency for Research on Cancer, (IARC)
Joint Expert Committee on Food Additives, (JECFA)
Journal of the American Medical Association
Journal of the American College of Toxicology
Lancet, The
Leading Edge Research
Material Safety Data Sheets, (MSDS) from numerous sources
National Center for Environmental Health
National Food Safety Database
National Institutes of Health (NIH), (USA)
National Institute of Occupational Safety and Health (NIOSH)
National Libraries of Medicine (USA)
National Resources Defence Council
National Toxicology Program (USA), (NTC)
Organic Consumers Association
Organic Federation of Australia
Registry of Toxic Effects of Chemical Substances, The, (RTECS)
Sax & Lewis "Dangerous Properties of Industrial Materials" Seventh Edition
Sargeant, Doris and Karen Evans, "Hard to Swallow - The Truth About Food Additives", *Alive Books*, 1999
Steinman, David and Samuel S Epstein "The Safe Shopper's Bible" *Macmillan*, 1995
Taubert, P.M., "Silent Killers" *CompSafe Consultancy*, 2001
Taubert, P.M., "Your Health and Food Additives - 2000 Edition" *CompSafe Consultancy*
Taubert, P.M., "Read the Label Know the Risks", *CompSafe Consultancy*, 2004
Total Environment Centre, "A-Z of Chemicals in the Home", 4th edition
Winter, Ruth M.S., "A Consumer's Dictionary of Cosmetic Ingredients - Sixth Edition" *Three Rivers Press*, 2005
Winter, Ruth M.S., "A Consumer's Dictionary of Food Additives - Sixth Edition" *Three Rivers Press*, 2004

Alphabetical List of Food Additives with Code Numbers

Additive Name	Code Number
Acacia or gum Arabic	414
Acesulphame potassium	950
Acetic acid, glacial	260
Acetic and fatty acid esters of glycerol	472a
Acetylated distarch adipate	1422
Acetylated distarch phosphate	1414
Acid treated starch	1401
Adipic acid	355
Agar	406
Alginic acid	400
Alitame	956
Alkaline treated starch	1402
Alkanet or Alkannin	103
Allura red AC	129
Aluminium	173
Aluminium, calcium, sodium, magnesium, potassium and ammonium salts of fatty acids	470
Aluminium silicate	559
Amaranth	123
Ammonium acetate	264
Ammonium adipates	359
Ammonium alginate	403
Ammonium bicarbonate	503
Ammonium chloride	510
Ammonium citrate	380
Ammonium fumarate	368
Ammonium hydrogen carbonate	503
Ammonium lactate	328
Ammonium malate	349
Ammonium phosphate	342
Ammonium salts of phosphatidic acid	442
α–Amylase	1100
Annatto extracts	160b
Anthocyanins or Grape skin extract or Blackcurrant extract	163
Arabinogalactan or Larch gum	409
Ascorbic acid	300

Ascorbyl palmitate	304
Aspartame	951
Azorubine or Carmoisine	122
β –apo-8' Carotenoic acid methyl or ethyl ester	160f
β –apo-8' Carotenal	160e
Beeswax, white and yellow	901
Beet red	162
Bentonite	558
Benzoic acid	210
Bleached starch	1403
Bone phosphate	542
Brilliant black BN or Brilliant black PN	151
Brilliant blue FCF	133
Brown HT	155
Butane	943a
Butylated hydroxyanisole (BHA)	320
Butylated hydroxytoluene (BHT)	321
Calcium acetate	263
Calcium alginate	404
Calcium aluminium silicate	556
Calcium ascorbate	302
Calcium benzoate	213
Calcium carbonate	170
Calcium chloride	509
Calcium citrate	333
Calcium disodium ethylenediaminetetraacetate or calcium disodium EDTA	385
Calcium fumarate	367
Calcium gluconate	578
Calcium glutamate	623
Calcium hydroxide	526
Calcium lactate	327
Calcium lactylate	482
Calcium malate	352
Calcium oleyl lactylate	482
Calcium oxide	529
Calcium phosphate	341
Calcium propionate	282
Calcium silicate	552
Calcium sorbate	203
Calcium stearoyl lactylate	482

Calcium sulphate	516
Calcium tartrate	354
Caramel I	150a
Caramel II	150b
Caramel III	150c
Caramel IV	150d
Carbon blacks or Vegetable carbon	153
Carbon dioxide	290
Carnauba wax	903
Carotene	160a
Carrageenan	407
Cellulose microcrystalline; cellulose, powdered	460
Chlorophyll	140
Chlorophyll-copper complex; chlorophyllin copper complex	141
Choline salts	1001
Citric acid	330
Citric and fatty acid esters of glycerol	472c
Cochineal or carmines or carminic acid	120
Cupric sulphate	519
Curcumin or turmeric	100
Cyclamate or calcium cyclamate or sodium cyclamate	952
Dextrin roasted starch	1400
Diacetyltartaric and fatty acid esters of glycerol	472e
Dimethyl dicarbonate	242
Dimethylpolysiloxane	900
Dioctyl sodium sulphosuccinate	480
Disodium 5'- ribonucleotides	635
Disodium 5'- guanylate	627
Disodium 5'- inosinate	631
Distarch phosphate	1412
Dodecyl gallate	312
Enzyme treated starches	1405
Erythorbic acid	315
Erythritol	968
Erythrosine	127
Ethyl maltol	637
Fast green FCF	143
Ferrous gluconate	579
Flavoxanthin	161a
Fumaric acid	297

Gellan gum 418
Glucono-δ-lactone or Glucono-delta-lactone 575
Glucose oxidase 1102
L-glutamic acid 620
Glycerin, glycerol 422
Glycerol esters of wood rosins 445
Glycine 640
Gold 175
Green S 142
Guar gum 412

4-hexylresorcinol 586
Hydrochloric acid 507
Hydroxypropyl cellulose 463
Hydroxypropyl distarch phosphate 1442
Hydroxypropyl methylcellulose 464
Hydroxypropyl starch 1440

Indigotine 132
Iron oxide 172
Isobutane 943b
Isomalt 953

Karaya gum 416
Kryptoxanthin 161c

L-Cysteine monohydrochloride 920
L-glutamic acid 620
L-Leucine 641
Lactic acid 270
Lactic and fatty acid esters of glycerol 472b
Lactitol 966
Lecithin 322
Lipases 1104
Locust bean gum or carob bean gum 410
Lutein 161b
Lycopene 160d
Lysozyme 1105

Magnesium carbonate 504
Magnesium chloride 511
Magnesium gluconate 580
Magnesium glutamate 625

Magnesium lactate	329
Magnesium oxide	530
Magnesium phosphate	343
Magnesium silicate or talc	553
Magnesium sulphate	518
Malic acid	296
Maltitol and maltitol syrup or hydrogenated glucose syrup	965
Maltol	636
Mannitol	421
Metatartaric acid	353
Methyl ethyl cellulose	465
Methylcellulose	461
Methylparaben or methyl-p-hydroxybenzoate	218
Mixed tartaric, acetic and fatty acid esters of glycerol	472f
Mono and diglycerides of fatty acids	471
Monoammonium-L-glutamate	624
Monopotassium L-glutamate	622
Monosodium L-glutamate or MSG	621
Mono starch phosphate	1410
Natamycin or pimaricin	235
Neotame	961
Nisin	234
Nitrogen	941
Nitrous oxide	942
Octafluorocyclobutane	946
Octyl gallate	311
Oxidised polyethylene	914
Oxidised starch	1404
Paprika oleoresins	160c
Pectin	440
Petrolatum or petroleum jelly	905b
Phosphated distarch phosphate	1413
Phosphoric acid	338
Polydextrose	1200
Polydimethylsiloxane or dimethylpolysiloxane	900a
Polyethylene glycol 8000	1521
Polyglycerol esters of fatty acids	475
Polyglycerol esters of interesterified ricinoleic acid	476
Polyoxyethylene (40) stearate	431
Polysorbate 60 or Polyoxyethylene (20) sorbitan monostearate	435

Polysorbate 65 or Polyoxyethylene (20) sorbitan tristearate	436
Polysorbate 80 or Polyoxyethylene (20) sorbitan monooleate	433
Polyvinylpyrrolidone	1201
Ponceau 4R	124
Potassium acetate or Potassium diacetate	261
Potassium adipate	357
Potassium alginate	402
Potassium aluminium silicate	555
Potassium ascorbate	303
Potassium benzoate	212
Potassium bicarbonate	501
Potassium bisulphite	228
Potassium chloride	508
Potassium citrate; potassium dihydrogen citrate	332
Potassium ferrocyanide	536
Potassium fumarate	366
Potassium gluconate	577
Potassium lactate	326
Potassium malate	351
Potassium metabisulphite	224
Potassium nitrate	252
Potassium nitrite	249
Potassium phosphate	340
Potassium polymetaphosphate	452
Potassium propionate	283
Potassium pyrophosphate	450
Potassium silicate	560
Potassium sodium tartrate	337
Potassium sorbate	202
Potassium sulphate	515
Potassium sulphite	225
Potassium tartrate or Potassium acid tartrate	336
Potassium tripolyphosphate	451
Processed eucheuma seaweed	407a
Propane	944
Propionic acid	280
Propyl gallate	310
Propylene glycol	1520
Propylene glycol alginate	405
Propylene glycol mono- and di-esters or Propylene glycol esters of fatty acids	477
Propylparaben or Propyl-p-hydroxybenzoate	216
Proteases (papain, bromelain, ficin)	1101

Quinoline yellow 104

Rhodoxanthin 161f
Riboflavin; Riboflavin 5'-phosphate sodium 101
Rubixanthin 161d

Saccharin or calcium saccharine or sodium saccharine or potassium saccharine 954
Saffron or crocetin or crocin 164
Shellac 904
Silicon dioxide, amorphous 551
Silver 174
Sodium acetate 262
Sodium acid pyrophosphate 450
Sodium alginate 401
Sodium aluminium phosphate 541
Sodium aluminosilicate 554
Sodium ascorbate 301
Sodium benzoate 211
Sodium bicarbonate 500
Sodium bisulphite 222
Sodium carbonate 500
Sodium carboxymethylcellulose 466
Sodium citrate 331
Sodium diacetate 262
Sodium dihydrogen citrate 331
Sodium erythorbate 316
Sodium ferrocyanide 535
Sodium fumarate 365
Sodium hydrogen malate 350
Sodium lactate 325
Sodium lactylate 481
Sodium malate 350
Sodium metabisulphite 223
Sodium metaphosphate, insoluble 452
Sodium nitrate 251
Sodium nitrite 250
Sodium oleyl lactylate 481
Sodium phosphate 339
Sodium polyphosphates, glassy 452
Sodium propionate 281
Sodium pyrophosphate 450
Sodium sorbate 201

Sodium stearoyl lactylate 481
Sodium sulphate 514
Sodium sulphite 221
Sodium tartrate 335
Sodium tripolyphosphate 451
Sorbic acid 200
Sorbitan monostearate 491
Sorbitan tristearate 492
Sorbitol or Sorbitol syrup 420
Stannous chloride 512
Starch acetate 1420
Starch sodium octenylsuccinate 1450
Stearic acid or fatty acid 570
Succinic acid 363
Sucralose 955
Sucrose acetate isobutyrate 444
Sucrose esters of fatty acids 473
Sulphur dioxide 220
Sunset yellow FCF 110

Talc or Magnesium silicate 553
Tannic acid or Tannins 181
Tartaric acid 334
Tartrazine 102
tert-Butylhydroquinone 319
Thaumatin 957
Titanium dioxide 171
α-Tocopherol 307
δ-Tocopherol 309
γ-Tocopherol 308
Tocopherols concentrate, mixed 306
Tragacanth gum 413
Triacetin 1518
Triammonium citrate 380
Triethyl citrate 1505

Violoxanthin 161e

Xanthan gum 415

Xylitol 967

Other Publications of POSSIBILITY.COM

THE CHEMICAL MAZE BOOKSHELF COMPANION
Your Guide to Food Additives and Cosmetic Ingredients
Bill Statham

ISBN 0 9578535 4 8

All the information contained in The Chemical Maze Shopping Companion and more. There is information on contaminants in foods and personal care products, genetic modification simplified, common ailments and the additives and ingredients most likely to cause or aggravate them, hidden additives and much more.

Now you can have two guides - The Chemical Maze Shopping Companion to keep in your shopping bag or the car, and the large print version, The Chemical Maze Bookshelf Companion, on your bookshelf for further reference.

Available December 2005

Happy High Herbs

ISBN 0 9578535 1 3

Ray Thorpe

Happy High Herbs is about happy high herbs, herbs that are currently available in Australia whether native, Australian grown or imported. The herbs described are happy highs because they are uplifting and generally mildly euphoric without the comedown, hangover or side effects that chemical drugs can give. Certainly none of them are addictive.

The ritual, cultural and medicinal uses, effects and precautions for over fifty herbs are outlined. Harm reduction tables give natural methods for overcoming harmful and/or addictive drugs.

Through the pages of this book, the author welcomes you on a journey back to nature and its wonderful bountiful harvest.

For more information visit www.happyhighherbs.com or contact the publisher.

Contact Information

POSSIBILITY.COM
E-mail: bill@possibilityoz.com
Website: www.thechemicalmaze.com

Visit our website for information on safer foods, cosmetics and personal care products.

Five per cent of the revenue from book sales will be donated to registered organizations supporting human and environmental health.